THE GAME'S AFOOT!

Now, match wits with the world's greatest consulting detective. And have no fear — if you don't completely succeed at first, just play again! It might be wise to keep in mind Holmes' advice to Watson and all would-be detectives:

> *"It is an old maxim of mine," he said, "that when you have eliminated the impossible, whatever remains, however improbable, must be the truth."*

SHERLOCK HOLMES SOLO MYSTERIES™ —developed by Iron Crown Enterprises — present a series of living mystery novels designed for solitary game play. In each gamebook, the reader is the detective who must solve or prevent a crime — with Sherlock Holmes and Dr. Watson as allies.

Murder at the Diogenes Club $2.95
The Black River Emerald $2.95
Death at Appledore Towers $2.95

Look for a new gamebook in the SHERLOCK HOLMES SOLO MYSTERIES™ series every other month from Berkley and Iron Crown Enterprises!

The Crown VS Dr. Watson $2.95
The Dynamiters $2.95

System Editor: S. Coleman Charlton

Editorial Contributions: Rob Bell, Kathy Conners, Jessica Ney

Production: Rob Bell, Richard H. Britton, Coleman Charlton, Kurt Fischer, Jessica Ney, John Ruemmler Suzanne Young

Sherlock Holmes was created by the late Sir Arthur Conan Doyle and appears in novels and stories by him

Grateful acknowledgement to Dame Jean Conan Doyle for permission to use the Sherlock Holmes characters created by Sir Arthur Conan Doyle

ISBN- 0-425-10617-9

PRINTED IN THE UNITED STATES OF AMERICA

Distributed by The Berkley Publishing Group, 200 Madison Avenue, New York, New York, 10016.

SHERLOCK HOLMES
SOLO MYSTERIES™

DEATH AT APPLEDORE TOWERS

by Gerald Lientz

Content Editor: John David Ruemmler
Managing Editor: Kevin Barrett
Cover Art &Illustrations by Daniel Horne

BERKLEY BOOKS, NEW YORK

CHARACTER RECORD

Name: DAVID PHILLIPS

Skill	Bonus
Athletics	+1
Artifice	+1
Observation	+1
Intuition	+1
Communication	+1
Scholarship	+1

Money:

6	pence
5	shillings
	guineas
2	pounds

Equipment:

1) POCKET KNIFE
2) PENCIL
3) NOTEBOOK
4)
5)
6)
7)
8)
9)
10)
11)

NOTES:

CHARACTER RECORD

Name:	

Skill	Bonus	Equipment:
Athletics	____	1)
Artifice	____	2)
Observation	____	3)
Intuition	____	4)
Communication	____	5)
Scholarship	____	6)
		7)
Money:	____pence	8)
	____shillings	9)
	____guineas	10)
	____pounds	11)

NOTES:

CLUE SHEET

- ☐ A ____________________
- ☐ B ____________________
- ☐ C ____________________
- ☐ D ____________________
- ☐ E ____________________
- ☐ F ____________________
- ☐ G ____________________
- ☐ H ____________________
- ☐ I ____________________
- ☐ J ____________________
- ☐ K ____________________
- ☐ L ____________________
- ☐ M ____________________
- ☐ N ____________________
- ☐ O ____________________
- ☐ P ____________________
- ☐ Q ____________________
- ☐ R ____________________
- ☐ S ____________________
- ☐ T ____________________
- ☐ U ____________________
- ☐ V ____________________
- ☐ W ____________________
- ☐ X ____________________
- ☐ Y ____________________
- ☐ Z ____________________
- ☐ AA ____________________
- ☐ BB ____________________
- ☐ CC ____________________

DECISIONS & DEDUCTIONS SHEET

❑ 1 ______________________________

❑ 2 ______________________________

❑ 3 ______________________________

❑ 4 ______________________________

❑ 5 ______________________________

❑ 6 ______________________________

❑ 7 ______________________________

❑ 8 ______________________________

❑ 9 ______________________________

❑ 10 ______________________________

❑ 11 ______________________________

❑ 12 ______________________________

❑ 13 ______________________________

❑ 14 ______________________________

❑ 15 ______________________________

❑ 16 ______________________________

❑ 17 ______________________________

❑ 18 ______________________________

❑ 19 ______________________________

❑ 20 ______________________________

❑ 21 ______________________________

❑ 22 ______________________________

❑ 23 ______________________________

❑ 24 ______________________________

❑ 25 ______________________________

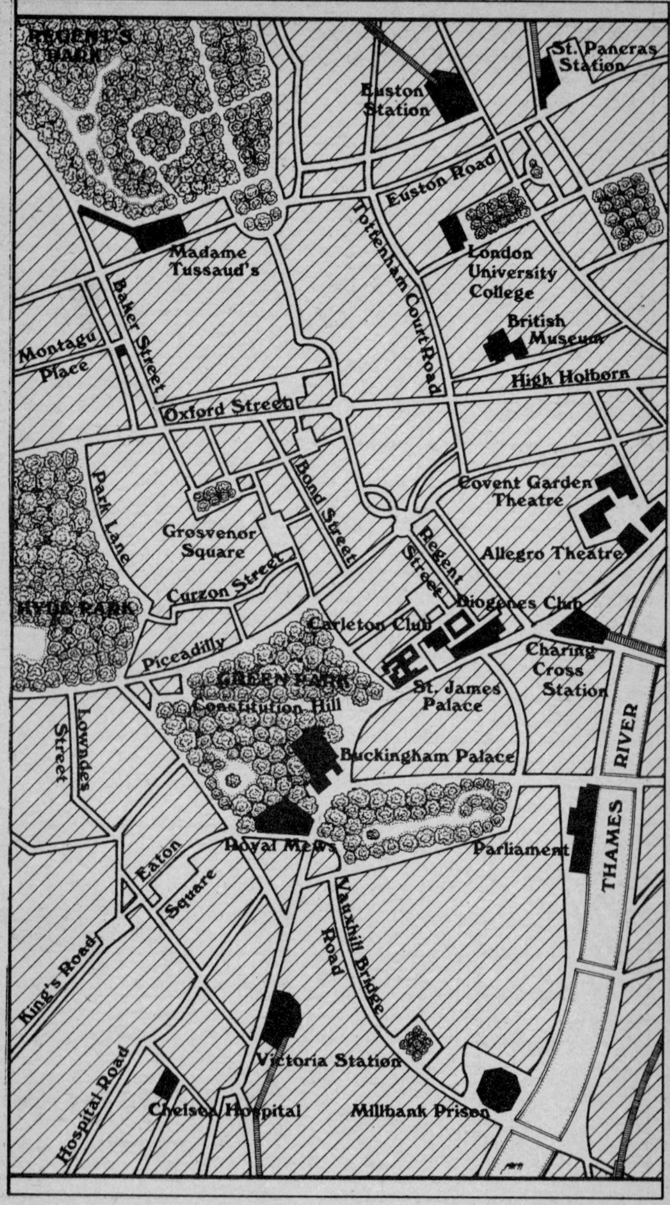
St. Pancras Station
Euston Station
Euston Road
Madame Tussaud's
Tottenham Court Road
London University College
British Museum
Montagu Place
Baker Street
High Holborn
Oxford Street
Bond Street
Park Lane
Covent Garden Theatre
Grosvenor Square
Regent Street
Allegro Theatre
Curzon Street
Diogenes Club
Carleton Club
Piccadilly
Charing Cross Station
St. James Palace
Constitution Hill
Lowndes Street
Buckingham Palace
RIVER
THAMES
Royal Mews
Parliament
Eaton Square
Vauxhill Bridge Road
King's Road
Victoria Station
Hospital Road
Chelsea Hospital
Millbank Prison

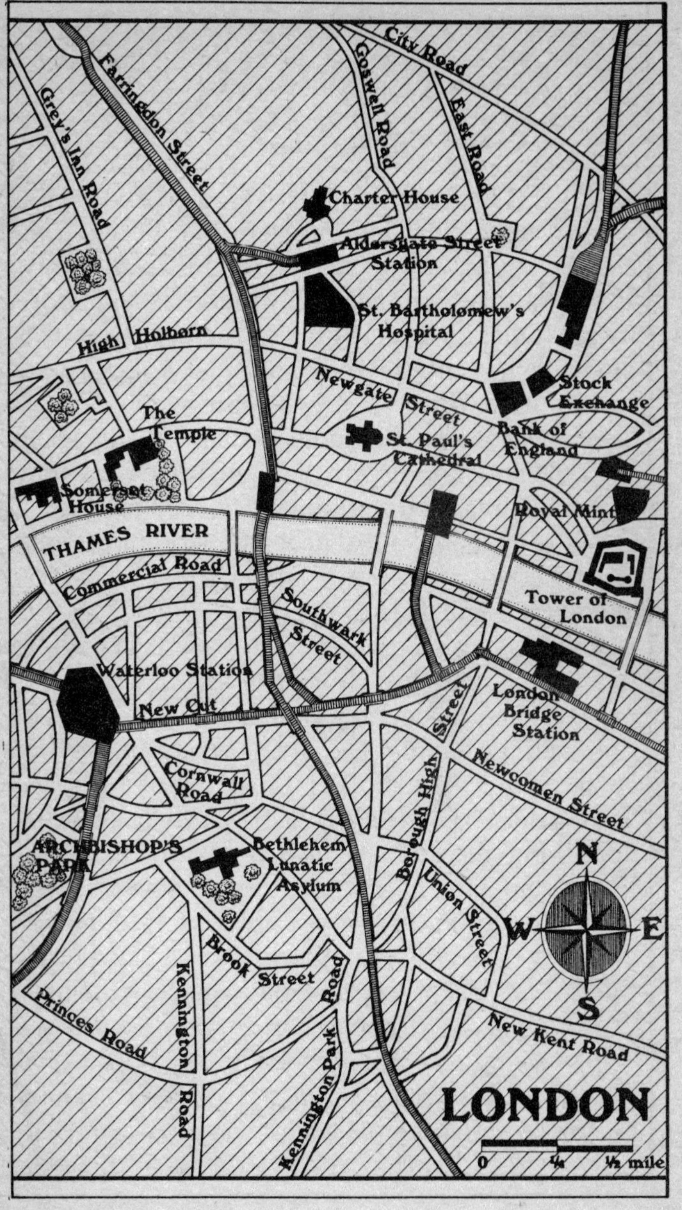
City Road
Goswell Road
East Road
Farringdon Street
Grey's Inn Road
Charter House
Aldersgate Street Station
St. Bartholomew's Hospital
High Holborn
Newgate Street
Stock Exchange
Bank of England
The Temple
St. Paul's Cathedral
Somerset House
Royal Mint
THAMES RIVER
Commercial Road
Tower of London
Southwark Street
Waterloo Station
New Cut
London Bridge Station
Street
Cornwall Road
Newcomen Street
Borough High
ARCHBISHOP'S PARK
Bethlehem Lunatic Asylum
Union Street
N
W
E
S
Brook Street
Kennington Road
Kennington Park Road
Princes Road
New Kent Road
LONDON
0
¼
½ mile

AN INTRODUCTION TO THE WORLD OF SHERLOCK HOLMES

HOLMES AND WATSON

First appearing in "A Study in Scarlet" in Beeton's Christmas Annual of 1887, Sherlock Holmes remains a remarkably vigorous and fascinating figure for a man of such advanced years. The detective's home and office at 221B Baker Street are shrines now, not simply rooms in which Holmes slept and deduced and fiddled with the violin when he could not quite discern the significance of a clue or put his finger on a criminal's twisted motive.

We know both a great deal and very little about Sherlock Holmes as a person. The son of a country squire (and grandson of the French artist Vernet's sister), Holmes seems to have drawn little attention to himself until his University days, where his extraordinary talents for applying logic, observation and deduction to solving petty mysteries earned him a reputation as something of a genius. Taking the next logical step, Holmes set up a private consulting detective service, probably in 1878. Four years later, he met and formed a partnership with a former military surgeon, Dr. John Watson. Four novels and fifty-six short stories tell us everything we know of the odd pair and their extraordinary adventures.

Less a well-rounded individual than a collection of contradictory and unusual traits, Holmes seldom exercised yet was a powerful man of exceptional speed of foot. He would eagerly work for days on a case with no rest and little food, yet in periods of idleness would refuse to get out of bed for days. Perhaps his most telling comment appears in "The Adventure of the Mazarin Stone:"

I am a brain, Watson. The rest of me is a mere appendix.

Holmes cared little for abstract knowledge, once noting that it mattered not to him if the earth circled the sun or vice versa. Yet he could identify scores of types of tobacco ash or perfume by sight and odor, respectively. Criminals and their modus operandi obsessed him; he pored over London's sensational newspapers religiously.

A master of disguise, the detective successfully presented himself as an aged Italian priest, a drunken groom, and even an old woman! A flabbergasted Watson is the perfect foil to Holmes, who seems to take special delight in astonishing his stuffy if kind cohort.

In "The Sign of Four," Holmes briefly noted the qualities any good detective should possess in abundance (if possible, intuitively): heightened powers of observation and deduction, and a broad range of precise (and often unusual) knowledge. In this ***Sherlock Holmes Solo Mysteries***™ adventure, you will have ample opportunity to test yourself in these areas, and through replaying the adventure, to improve your detective skills.

Although impressive in talent and dedication to his profession, Sherlock Holmes was by no means perfect. Outfoxed by Irene Adler, Holmes readily acknowledged defeat by "the woman" in "A Scandal in Bohemia." In 1887, he admitted to Watson that three men had outwitted him (and Scotland Yard). The lesson Holmes himself drew from these failures was illuminating:

> *Perhaps when a man has special knowledge and special powers like my own, it rather encourages him to seek a complex explanation when a simpler one is at hand.*

So learn to trust your own observations and deductions — when they make sense and match the physical evidence and the testimony of trusted individuals — don't rush to judgment, and if you like and the adventure allows, consult Holmes or Watson for advice and assistance.

VICTORIAN LONDON

When Holmes lived and worked in London, from the early 1880's until 1903, the Victorian Age was much more than a subject of study and amusement. Queen Victoria reigned over England for more than 60 years, an unheard of term of rule; her tastes and inhibitions mirrored and formed those of English society. Following the Industrial Revolution of roughly 1750-1850, England leaped and stumbled her way from a largely pastoral state into a powerful, flawed factory of a nation. (The novels of Charles Dickens dramatically depict this cruel, exhilarating period of sudden social change.) Abroad, imperialism planted the Union Jack (and implanted English mores) in Africa, India, and the Far East, including Afghanistan, where Dr. Watson served and was wounded.

Cosmopolitan and yet reserved, London in the late Nineteenth Century sported over six million inhabitants, many from all over the world; it boasted the high society of Park Lane yet harbored a seedy Chinatown where opium could be purchased and consumed like tea. To orient yourself, Consult the two-page map of London on pages 10 and 11. You will see that Baker Street is located just south of Regent's Park, near the Zoological Gardens, in the heart of the stylish West End of the city. Railway and horse-drawn carriages were the preferred means of transport; people often walked, and thieves frequently ran to get from one place to another.

THE GAME'S AFOOT!

Now, match wits with the world's greatest consulting detective. And have no fear — if you don't completely succeed at first, just play again! It might be wise to keep in mind Holmes' advice to Watson and all would-be detectives:

> *"It is an old maxim of mine," he said, "that when you have eliminated the impossible, whatever remains, however improbable, must be the truth."*

Good luck and good hunting!

THE *SHERLOCK HOLMES SOLO MYSTERIES*™ GAME SYSTEM

THE GAMEBOOK

This gamebook describes hazards, situations, and locations that may be encountered during your adventures. As you read the text sections, you will be given choices as to what actions you may take. What text section you read will depend on the directions in the text and whether the actions you attempt succeed or fail.

Text sections are labeled with three-digit numbers (e.g.,"365"). Read each text section only when told to do so by the text.

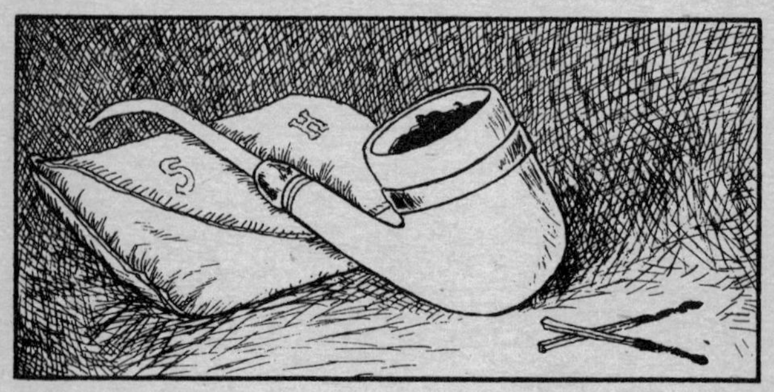

PICKING A NUMBER

Many times during your adventures in this gamebook you will need to pick a number (between 2 and 12). There are several ways to do this:

1) Turn to the Random Number Table at the end of this book, use a pencil (or pen or similar object), close your eyes, and touch the Random Number Table with the pencil. The number touched is the number which you have picked. If your pencil falls on a line, just repeat the process. **or**

2) Flip to a random page in the book and look at the small boxed number in the inside, bottom corner of the page. This number is the number which you have picked. **or**

3) If you have two six-sided dice, roll them. The result is the number which you have picked. (You can also roll one six-sided die twice and add the results.)

Often you will be instructed to pick a number and add a "bonus". When this happens, treat results of more than 12 as "12" and treat results of less than 2 as "2".

3

INFORMATION, CLUES, AND SOLVING THE MYSTERY

During play you will discover certain clues (e.g., a footprint, murder weapon, a newspaper article) and make certain decisions and deductions (e.g., you decide to follow someone, you deduce that the butler did it). Often the text will instruct you to do one of the following:

Check Clue xx or ***Check Decision xx*** or ***Check Deduction xx.***

"xx" is a letter for Clues and a number for Decisions and Deductions. When this occurs, check the appropriate box on the "Clue Record Sheets" found at the beginning of the book. You should also record the information gained and note the text section number on the line next to the box. You may copy or photocopy these sheets for your own use.

Other useful information not requiring a "check" will also be included in the text. You may want to take other notes, so a "NOTES" space is provided at the bottom of your "Character Record". Remember that some of the clues and information given may be meaningless or unimportant (i.e., red herrings).

EQUIPMENT AND MONEY

Whenever you acquire money and equipment, record them on your Character Record in the spaces provided. Pennies (1 Pence), shillings (12 pence), guineas (21 shillings), and pounds (20 shillings) are "money" and may be used during your adventures to pay for food, lodging, transport, bribes, etc. Certain equipment may affect your abilities as indicated by the text.

You begin the adventure with the money noted on the completed Character Record sheet near the front of the book.

CHOOSING A CHARACTER

There are two ways to choose a character:

1) You can use the completely created character provided at the beginning of the book. **or**

2) You can create your own character using the simple character development system included in the next section of this book.

STARTING TO PLAY

After reading the rules above and choosing a character to play, start your adventures by reading the Prologue found after the rules section. From this point on, read the passages as indicated by the text.

CREATING YOUR OWN CHARACTER

If you do not want to create your own character, use the pre-created character found in the front of this book. If you decide to create your own character, follow the directions given in this section. Keep track of your character on the blank Character Record found in the front of this book. It is advisable to enter information in pencil so that it can be erased and updated. If necessary, you may copy or photocopy this Character Record for your own use.

As you go through this character creation process, refer to the pre-created character in the front of the book as an example.

SKILLS

The following 6 "Skill Areas" affect your chances of accomplishing certain actions during your adventures.

1) **Athletics** (includes fitness, adroitness, fortitude, pugnacity, fisticuffs): This skill reflects your ability to perform actions and maneuvers requiring balance, coordination, speed, agility, and quickness. Such actions can include fighting, avoiding attacks, running, climbing, riding, swimming, etc.
2) **Artifice** (includes trickery, disguise, stealth, eavesdropping): Use this skill when trying to move without being seen or heard (i.e., sneaking), trying to steal something, picking a lock, escaping from bonds, disguising yourself, and many other similar activities.
3) **Intuition** (includes sensibility, insight, reasoning, deduction, luck): This skill reflects your ability to understand and correlate information, clues, etc. It also reflects your ability to make guesses and to have hunches.
4) **Communication** (includes interviewing, acting, mingling, negotiating, diplomacy): This skill reflects your ability to talk with, negotiate with, and gain information from people. It also reflects your "social graces" and social adaptivity, as well as your ability to act and to hide your own thoughts and feelings.

5) **Observation** (includes perception, alertness, empathy): This skill reflects how much information you gather through visual perception.

6) **Scholarship** (includes education, science, current events, languages): This skill reflects your training and aptitude with various studies and sciences: foreign languages, art, history, current events, chemistry, tobaccory, biology, etc.

SKILL BONUSES

For each of these skills, you will have a Skill Bonus that is used when you attempt certain actions. When the text instructs you to "add your bonus," it is referring to these Skill Bonuses. Keep in mind that these "bonuses" can be negative as well as positive.

When you start your character, you have six "+1 bonuses" to assign to your skills.

You may assign more than one "+1 bonuses" to a given skill, but no more than three to any one skill. Thus, two "+1 bonuses" assigned to a skill will be a "+2 bonus", and three "+1 bonuses" will be a "+3 bonus". Each of these bonuses should be recorded in the space next to the appropriate skill on your Character Record.

If you do not assign any "+1 bonuses" to a skill, you must record a "-2 bonus" in that space.

During play you may acquire equipment or injuries that may affect your bonuses. Record these modifications in the "Bonus" spaces.

CAST OF CHARACTERS

The Countess d'Albert, a great lady of London.
Lord and Lady Beaverton, an estranged couple.
Bessie, the upstairs maid.
Lady Eva Blackwell, fiance of the Earl of Devoncourt.
Miss Phillippa Blackwell, cousin of Lady Eva.
Lady Blakeney, widow of a great statesman and general.
Mrs. Cox, the cook.
Lady Sylvia Daniels, recently cancelled her engagement.
Colonel Dorking, formerly fiance of Miss Miles.
Lord Ellington, a satisfied former employer.
Lieutenant John Fraser, a friend of Captain Grey.
Dr. Gordon, police surgeon at the morgue.
Green, the undergardener at Appledore Towers.
Captain Grey, an army officer stationed in London.
Helen, the kitchen maid.
Mr. Jenkins, Milverton's loyal secretary.
Johnny, the page.
Mary Jones, the house maid.
Inspector Lestrade of Scotland Yard.
Mrs. Lindon, the housekeeper.
Mr. Malone, foreman at the gasworks.
Miss Miles, a lady whose marriage plans were cancelled.
Charles Augustus Milverton,
murdered "agent," owner of Appledore Towers.
Mr. Osborne, a friend of Lestrade's and expert on scandal.
John and James Patterson, young men of London.
Reynolds, the coachman.
Shepherd, the footman.
Silversmith, butler at Appledore Towers.
Yates, the groom.

NOTE: *you have a pocket knife, a pencil, a notebook, and 2 pounds, 5 shillings and 6 pence when you begin the adventure. Note these items on your Character Record and begin your investigation.*

PROLOGUE

Recently, Lord Ellington, who heard of your skills from one of your satisfied clients, invited you to look into a problem of some missing papers. His Lordship feared the papers would be misused by the thief. To his satisfaction (and your own), you were able to trap the thief in a single night. To make your success all the greater, the thief stole some of his Lordship's silver, so that he could be arrested without embarrassing references to the stolen personal papers. Pleased with your discretion and skill, Lord Ellington has paid you well and promised he would give you full references any time you should need them. Accompanied by Lord Ellington and his valet, you take the villain to Cannon Row Police Station, where he is charged and locked away.

As you dispose of the matter, you see Inspector Lestrade hurry in, shouting orders and demanding the services of several constables and various other specialists. On seeing you, he hesitates, as though thinking for a moment. "I know you, don't I?" he mutters, looking a little puzzled. Then he nods. "Aye, you're Mr. Holmes protege, aren't you, the one he gives all the cases to when he is too busy to deal with them himself? It's fortunate we have the pair of you, so that London is kept safe from all the matters too complex for us poor silly policemen. What brings you to Cannon Row today?"

You are more than a little startled at the bitter irony in Lestrade's voice, for the Inspector usually admits the greatest respect for Holmes' skills. Before you reply, Lord Ellington comes to your defense. "You shouldn't be so rude to this young man, sir," his Lordship says sharply. "I am Lord Ellington. This gentleman has just settled a matter for me, and he did it so quickly and neatly that it seemed miraculous to me. The Mr. Holmes you mentioned could likely take lessons from him."

Lestrade laughs lightly, bowing to the peer as he leaves the police station, but the detective looks thoughtful. "Your skills seem to have improved since last we met," he says slowly. "I am sorry if I sounded brusque. I have been up most of the night dealing with an important case, a murder over near Hampstead

Heath. After spending the night at Appledore Towers looking into the matter, I stopped at Baker Street to ask Mr. Holmes for his help. He told me that he was deeply involved in a matter referred to him by the Prime Minister and could not possibly investigate another case until it was concluded."

With hope rising in your heart, you ask: "May I help you in the matter, Mr. Lestrade? I do not have Mr. Holmes' knowledge or skill, but if I could possibly be of assistance, I should be delighted to help."

"Holmes has schooled you in his methods," Lestrade mutters. "Well, come along; it may turn out that there are aspects to the case better investigated by someone without official connections." You turn and follow Lestrade into a cab, wondering who is dead, how, and why. ***Pick a number*** *and add your Intuition bonus:*

- *If 2-8,* ***turn to 164.***
- *If 9-12,* ***turn to 444.***

100

"I have heard the name, of course," she admits. "I read about the murder in the papers. But it couldn't have anything to do with me. My maid, Ellen, knows how silly it would be to blackmail me. The whole business is ludicrous." She laughs heartily and rings for her butler. With the sublime dignity of his trade, the butler shows you out. ***Turn to 456.***

101

You consider Mr. Jenkins's story and wonder what this careful little man has not told you. ***Pick a number*** *and add your Intuition bonus:*

- *If 2-7,* ***turn to 227.***
- *If 8-12,* ***turn to 608.***

102

Lestrade consults his list and tells you that Mrs. Cox, the cook, is next. "Will you talk to her?" he asks.

- *If you want to see the cook,* ***turn to 205.***
- *Otherwise,* ***turn to 505.***

103

"Thank you, Mr. Holmes," you chuckle, "I shall look for you the next time I need a cab."

The detective straightens and smiles. "Watson never spoils my fun by recognizing me," he chuckles. "When we saw your notice in the newspapers, I couldn't resist the temptation to test your powers of observation. But I waited to be certain that a genuine cabbie wasn't coming, so I didn't knock until the clocks struck ten." After another word or two, the detective leaves. ***Turn to 351.***

104

Though you try to be as thorough as possible, you find nothing of use in the little alcove. ***Turn to 476.***

105

You consider further questions for the brothers.

- *If you ask them about Milverton's murder,* ***turn to 434.***
- *Otherwise,* ***turn to 449.***

106

"I believe that Colonel Dorking killed Milverton," you say, "probably accompanied by his nephew when he went to Appledore Towers."

Holmes shakes his head, his face showing astonishment at the idea. "No, no," he says, "they couldn't have been involved. I happen to know that they played whist at his club until very late that night." ***Turn to 352.***

107

"Madame, after meeting you I do not see how he could have been connected to so fine a lady, but the late Mr. Milverton was a blackmailer. In all too many cases, the separation of a husband and wife would be a result of his actions. Because the man was murdered, I must speak to all possible victims."

"I see," she answers, a trifle grim. "Though I wonder why you should bother hunting the killer of such a villain. However, he had nothing to do with my husband's current behaviour. We disagreed on how much we should do for our younger son, and while he accepted my view that we must make the lad find his own way for a while, he does not want to see me for a few weeks while he sulks." You talk politely for a few minutes, but she obviously has little interest in you, and soon the butler shows you out. ***Turn to 463.***

108

"Countess," you answer, "someone must be told. After all, we cannot let one person kill another. We must at least know why he was killed and then judge whether the killer should be arrested." The Countess considers your arguments. ***Pick a number*** *and add your Communication bonus: (Add 2 if you checked Decision 20.)*

- *If 2-7,* ***turn to 120.***
- *If 8-12,* ***turn to 112.***

109

"I do not wish cause you concern," you continue, "but I am a little surprised that you feel so safe, even with Mr. Milverton's death. Some associate of his may still have the papers —"

10

"Oh no, that's not possible!" she interupts, then stops to think. "I mean," she continues, "he wouldn't have time now. And the police must have taken all of Milverton's letters." She looks desperately towards her cousin, but that grim lady has nothing to add. ***Pick a number** and add your Intuition bonus:*

- *If 2-5, **turn to 184**.*
- *If 6-12, **turn to 128**.*

110

"Perhaps I had heard of Appledore Towers," she says slowly, "as well as the late Mr. Milverton. But the case involves a friend of mine, and I doubt that I should trust you with someone else's secret. Why should I?" she asks sharply.

- *If you mention the importance of solving any murder, **turn to 108**.*
- *If you remind her of Lord Ellington's letter, **turn to 171**.*

111

"Miss Phillippa," you say carefully, "I am investigating the murder of a blackmailer, a man named Milverton. Unexpectedly, the name of Lady Eva came up in the course of the investigation, and because of her upcoming nuptials, it was thought best to talk to her immediately, and as quietly as possible."

Phillippa Blackwell studies you for a moment, then nods. "It is nonsense to think that she would know anything of any murder. But I will let you talk to her. However, if you hurt her in any way, I shall see to it that you regret the day you were born." ***Turn to 201**.*

112

The Countess listens to your argument, then agrees. "I will trust you," she says. "I should rather talk to you than to the police."

"Thank you," you answer. "How did you become involved with Milverton?"

"I am not involved with him at all," she answers, "but a friend of mine has some connection to him. Lady Blakeney came to me last week, and told me that she needed to correspond with this man Milverton without anyone knowing her involvement."

"An odd request, wasn't it?" you suggest.

"Not as odd as it might be," she answers. "My friends know that I mind my own business and will not chide them for their indiscretions. Lady Blakeney has not always been as careful in choosing help in delicate affairs. I agreed that if a note came to this house from Appledore Towers, I would enclose it in another envelope and send it over to her. The name on the envelope was a false one."

"And did you receive such a letter?" you ask.

She nods. "I received one the morning of the day that Milverton was killed. I sent it to Lady Blakeney, just as we had agreed." *Check Clue Z.* ***Turn to 121.***

113

"What sort of man was Mr. Milverton?" you ask the housemaid.

"Oh, that's not for me to say, is it sir?" she answers quickly. "It's not for someone in my position to judge an important man like him. I do know that he was very particular that his rooms be cleaned just the way he liked them, and that none of his drawers or anything be disturbed, but I've heard from my friends that almost all masters are like that." ***Turn to 326.***

114

"Miss Miles killed Milverton," you say confidently. "She hated him for destroying her marriage."

Holmes shakes his head. "There is simply no evidence to justify the charge," he tells you. ***Turn to 352.***

115

As soon as you decide to interview the Countess d'Albert, you wonder how you will deal with someone that important who does not have an immediate, obvious connection to the investigation. She might not even be willing to talk to you. ***Pick a number*** *and add your Intuition bonus:*

•*If 2-7,* ***turn to 617.***
•*If 8-12,* ***turn to 397.***

116

You hide behind a bush and wait for your helpers to earn their money. Angry shouts and crashing noises sound from down the street, then more shouting. Curious at the sound, Lady Blakeney's butler and cook run out of the house and down the street to see what is happening. As you had hoped, they leave the front door ajar. You slip through it and up the stairs.

Upstairs you quickly find what must be Lady Blakeney's room. It is furnished in a fashion that shows both great wealth and the finest taste. As you begin to search for evidence in the case, moving cautiously, you hear the butler and cook entering the house, chatting about the fight. ***Pick a number*** *and add your Artifice bonus:*

•*If 2-6,* ***turn to 122.***
•*If 7-12,* ***turn to 320.***

117

You face Jenkins. "Mr. Jenkins," you say, "you can inform us about one aspect of Mr. Milverton's life that no one else has been able to make clear. Exactly what kind of business did he engage in? We know he called himself an 'agent', but that is not a very descriptive title."

"I don't know how much more descriptive I could be sir," Jenkins answers. "He did the things an agent does. Arranged business deals where it was unwise for the parties to meet because of the effect on others, found things people wanted to buy for a fee, or found a proper buyer when someone had unusual merchandise to sell. He was very good at it — most of his customers were well satisfied."

"What kind of transactions did he arrange?" you ask.

"Oh, all kinds sir. Sale of jewels, of paintings sometimes, or rare manuscripts. Autographs were another of his lines, sir — you'd be surprised how many people are anxious to have a paper signed by a noted person."

"What was your part in this, Mr. Jenkins?" you continue.

"I wrote letters for him sir, to one party or the other; but they were very careful letters, sir. He seldom named the merchandise when he wrote, you see. He'd just ask me to write something like, 'I now have the items you were so desirous of obtaining, sir. I can let you have them at our agreed price until the 22nd.' That sort of missive."

•*If you checked Deduction 12, **turn to 343.***
•*Otherwise, **turn to 566.***

118

"You have been very helpful," you tell Jenkins, "and have increased our chances of catching the murderers. I have one more question: do you have any idea who had cause to kill Mr. Milverton?" ***Pick a number** and add your Communication bonus:*

•*If 2-5, **turn to 190.***
•*If 6-8, **turn to 574.***
•*If 9-12, **turn to 405.***

119

"I doubt that I should say anything more about the matter," the butler says stiffly. "It is hardly proper to talk about my employer's affairs."

You nod pleasantly. "Of course not," you agree. "I would not ask, ordinarily. But as you can see from my papers, I am investigating a delicate matter. You may well be able to give me information that would save me from disturbing Lady Blakeney when she is trying to rest."

The butler considers this, then says: "I would do anything to save her ladyship more trouble. The afternoon before she left, she received an odd letter from the Countess d'Albert. She opened it immediately; there was another envelope inside it. I was alarmed by the fire that leapt into her eyes then, but she subdued it. She went out that evening, to help a friend deal with a crisis, and returned home very late. I think dealing with her friend's problems helped her ease her own heart, for she was much calmer the next day." ***Turn to 294.***

120

The Countess shakes her head. "No, I cannot agree that the mention of my name is important," she says sharply. "Probably you misread the name, or the villain used my name as a code for some other victim. If you will excuse me, sir, I have a very busy day ahead." ***Turn to 121.***

121

You thank the Countess for her time, bow, and leave. ***Turn to 456.***

122

Searching the room you bump into a small table covered with a vase, two china dogs and a photograph of the late Lord Blakeney. Shouts from downstairs show that the house is alerted to your presence. Hurriedly you swing out a window and climb down the ivy. Before the servants can catch you you vault over the back wall. ***Pick a number:***

- *If 2-7,* ***turn to 533.***
- *If 8-12,* ***turn to 536.***

123

"Blackmail?" the Countess asks incredulously. "How could anyone blackmail me?"

"It seems that Milverton took some interest in you," you answer carefully.

"What if he did?" she snaps. "I will have you know that I have not done anything that would make me a target for that kind of villainy, young man. Apart from my innocence, I would not care what kind of threats a blackmailer made to me. There is no one whose opinion I value who would be influenced by such actions, nor any other way that Milverton could hurt me."

"Milverton had made an appointment for midnight with your maid," you say carefully. "We must try to examine why he was interested in you, as he was murdered." ***Pick a number and add your Communication bonus:***

- *If 2-7,* ***turn to 124.***
- *If 8-12,* ***turn to 133.***

124

The Countess shakes her head. "This entire affair is rubbish," she says. "I have no time to waste over this sort of nonsense. I have too much to do." She rings for the butler and orders him to show you out. ***Turn to 456.***

125

As the city's clocks chime ten o'clock, there is a knock at your door. When you answer a tall, thin man, bent over and walking with a noticeable limp, shuffles in. A dirty cap is pulled far down over his face, and the unshaven stubble on his cheeks is set off by the bright red nose of the hard drinker. From his breath you realize he had a drop of drink before he came to see you.

"Are you the bloke what put the note in the papers?" he demands. "The ad for the driver what picked up two gents on the heath the other night?" You nod. "Well, I'm your man," he goes on, "and I can settle your wager for you."

"Go ahead," you urge him.

"Well, it was like this," he says. "These two blokes comes off the heath and over to my cab, and asks me to carry them into town. Now that's natural enough, you says, but these two blokes was dressed like toffs, and drunk as lords, and they carried this bag that seemed to be moving. So's I told them that they'd have to pay me double fare on account of the bag, and they done it. Bought me an extra bottle of gin against the cold, that double money did. You figure that was your friends?"

- *If you pay him to get rid of him,* ***turn to 316.***
- *If you chase him off without money,* ***turn to 468.***
- *If you question him further,* ***turn to 336.***

126

Before checking the next name on his list, Lestrade asks Silversmith to send in tea and cakes, which you both find to be a good restorative. Lestrade tells you that the upstairs maid, Bessie, is the next member of the staff on his list.

- *If you want to see her,* ***turn to 196.***
- *Otherwise,* ***turn to 344.***

127

"Mrs. Lindon," you continue, "can you tell us something about your late master? What kind of man was he? Was there any reason why someone would want to kill him?" You wonder if you've asked the question tactfully. ***Pick a number*** *and add your Communication bonus:*

•*If 2-6,* ***turn to 609.***
•*If 7-12,* ***turn to 607.***

128

Lady Eva's explanation of her relief does not ring true to you. The newspaper accounts of the murder did not mention the destruction of Milverton's letters.

•*If you ask again why she feels safe,* ***turn to 415.***
•*Otherwise,* ***turn to 184.***

129

You begin to go over the area marked up by the footprints of the staff running from the front door. Fortunately, while the sun has begun to burn off the frost, the shadow of the house and wall have shaded this area. ***Pick a number*** *and add your Observation bonus: (Add 1 if you have Clue A)*

•*If 2-8,* ***turn to 340.***
•*If 9-12,* ***turn to 156.***

130

You remember the late night appointment Milverton had the night he was killed. "Mr. Silversmith," you ask, "was it common for Mr. Milverton to have visitors very late at night, say midnight or later?"

"Late visitors?" the butler answers. "Why, I don't know sir. There were never any who rang the front door bell, but the master had a private entrance into his study. I was never awake at that hour. I always turn in at eleven, and since I was a lad, I've always fallen asleep quickly."

"Did he ever ask you to leave a door unlocked?" Lestrade continues, glancing at you. "Did he give any special orders the night he died?"

"He had no need to have any door unlocked," Silversmith answered, "but some nights, maybe three or four times a year, he told me to have the men lock up the dog. In fact, he asked me to do that the night he was murdered, but he never told me why, and it was not my place to ask."

"Of course," you agree. Silversmith's discretion certainly suits his position. *Check Clue I.* ***Turn to 134.***

131

You decide that it would be a little untactful to ask Silversmith to talk about his late master's business. If Silversmith knows anything of the unsavory aspects of Milverton's affairs, he is far too discreet to discuss them.

•*If you ask him about the rest of the staff,* ***turn to 433.***
•*Otherwise,* ***turn to 448.***

132

You tell Lestrade that you think it more important to go ahead with the staff interviews than to see Milverton's body. Lestrade accepts your decision, calls the butler and explains what you need.

"Certainly, sir," Silversmith answers. "I asked the maid to ready a room for you, and I shall be certain that all the staff are available to you." ***Turn to 465.***

133

The Countess seems to think about the matter, then demands: "If I know something, why should I trust you? Are you a safe repository for such delicate information?"

•*If you tell her that murder must be solved,* **turn to 108.**
•*If you tell her you will review the case with Sherlock Holmes before telling the police,* ***turn to 141.***

134

You wonder whether Silversmith knew anything of his master's unsavory business affairs, and whether he might have an idea of who would have wanted Milverton dead.

•*If you ask him about Milverton's business affairs,* ***turn to 147.***

•*Otherwise,* ***turn to 131.***

135

While you feel that the evidence points to the intruders having killed Milverton, you must consider that there is a chance that someone else came into the study — possibly a woman. Perhaps she killed Milverton, and the "innocent" intruders fled. It is fairly clear that the two men did not have legitimate business at Appledore Towers, but perhaps the woman did. ***Turn to 247.***

136

"If you had to identify the two intruders, how would you go about it, Mr. Holmes?" you ask.

He considers the question for a moment. "There are two possible reasons for their going to Appledore Towers. Either they were victims of Mr. Milverton's blackmail who wished to destroy the evidence (and perhaps Mr. Milverton as well), or they were hired to go there and accomplish one task or the other."

"Which do you believe it to be?" you ask.

"Probably it was a victim, or the relative of a victim," he answers. "If they were hired, they would have to be men of the greatest discretion and good character, or else the person who hired them would be trading blackmail by Milverton for blackmail by the intruders. And there are not very many honest and discreet men who are also skillful burglars." Watson laughs at this last comment, and suggests that you talk of more pleasant things than events surrounding a murder. ***Turn to 277.***

137

It is only a little after nine when there is a knock at your door. You open it to admit a short, slender man, obviously a cab driver from his rough dress and horsy smell.

"Is this your ad?" he asks, almost shoving a paper in your face as he asks.

"Yes, it is," you agree. "Who was your strange passenger?"

"Well, I don't know her name sir," he answers, "but it was a very great lady, I think; tall and carried herself like a queen, very beautiful. Could see that even though she was wrapped in a cloak and had a veil down over her face. Passing strange to pick up a lady by herself like that, so late in the night. Not at any house, neither sir, but in the open. I asked no questions and she gave no answers."

"Where did you take her?" you ask, trying to keep your voice calm.

"I can't remember sir," he answers. "Rich folk don't want you to remember when you pick them up under odd circumstances. You pay the man his money and he quickly leaves. *Deduct 5 shillings from your Character Record. Check Clue S.* ***Pick a number:***

- *If 2-5,* ***turn to 535.***
- *If 6-12,* ***turn to 351.***

138

Once you are satisfied that the drive will furnish no more information, Lestrade leads you to the area outside Milverton's bedroom and study. The police detective is very careful to walk along some boards laid close to the house, and suggests you do the same to protect the multitude of tracks on the ground. A tiled veranda runs along the wall outside Milverton's rooms. Here Lestrade stops and asks Silversmith to explain the layout of the grounds to you.

The butler agrees. "This door leads into the master's study. There is also an entrance from the inside of the house. When we heard the shots last night, we tried the inside door and found it locked. We then circled back through the house, out the front door, and rushed to this area." The butler points and you can see the marks on the frosted grass made by the servants as they ran toward the veranda. "Just as we neared the outer door of the study," Silversmith continues, "one of us saw two men running from the far end of the veranda into the garden. We pursued them, but they seemed to know the grounds very well, and escaped over the wall before we could seize them." As the butler pauses, you consider which group of tracks you should examine first.

•*If you examine the servants' tracks,* ***turn to 359.***
•*If you follow the intruders' tracks,* ***turn to 381.***

139

You thank the cabbie for his help and pay him his reward. *Deduct 5 shillings from your Character Record.* ***Turn to 351.***

140

You wonder what information the butler might have, and even more, what information he might be willing to tell. His discretion is obvious. ***Turn to 178.***

141

"I share your concern," you say carefully. "But while I am working with the police in this case, I understand that the murder of a blackmailer must be investigated with the greatest possible discretion. Before I present the police with a solution, I will discuss the matter with Mr. Sherlock Holmes. His reputation is such that anyone may trust him to treat the matter with all due discretion. I will follow his advice to insure that no innocent person is hurt by what I learn." ***Pick a number*** *and add your Communication bonus:*

•*If 2-7,* ***turn to 120.***
•*If 8-12,* ***turn to 112.***

142

Your efforts to hunt down the plumber, Escott, have taken you virtually the whole day. The sun is going down as you return to your quarters. You go to bed early, and rise early the next day to pursue further steps in the case. ***Turn to 278.***

143

"I never heard of the man," Gray says after a pause, "and I don't care for the tone of your question. Corporal Fowler!" he shouts to the orderly, "Come show the gentleman out please." The orderly comes in and quickly leads you out, escorting you until you are outside the barracks. ***Turn to 230.***

144

You lean forward in the growler as Lestrade speaks. "The murder victim is Mr. Charles Augustus Milverton of Appledore Towers. He was killed by two men who entered his study last night around midnight. The men fired half a dozen shots into Milverton's chest, and burned many of his papers. The servants naturally were aroused by the shots, and the killers fled through the garden. They made it over the wall just ahead of Milverton's men—in fact the undergardener got a hand on one of the killers for a moment. I will allow you to interview the staff and go over the ground yourself. I know Mr. Holmes insists that he see the evidence for himself rather than hear a description of it from me."

[7]

"Very well," you agree. "But you said that Mr. Milverton was a blackmailer. Can you tell me any more about his activities?'

Lestrade hesitates, then nods. "That is one of the major problems with this case. We had strong reason to suspect that Milverton was involved in the blackmail of many people high in society, the very cream of the upper class. But it did us no good. The man was too clever to allow us to uncover evidence of his misdeeds. You must be careful when you search for those with a reason to kill him. Many of his victims will be pleased when they read of his death, and will be anxious to hide their connection to him. You may have an advantage as an unofficial agent—they may talk to you, knowing that you can be more discreet than the police. You may be forced to use my name as leverage to make some of them talk — threaten them with a visit from me if they don't cooperate with you." Lestrade smiles a little. You try to order your thoughts to begin a scientific investigation of what happened last night.

The growler rumbles to a stop and the driver opens the door for you and Lestrade. "Appledore Towers," he announces, and you descend outside the gates of the estate. ***Turn to 559.***

145

"Helen," you begin, "please tell me what you thought of Mr. Milverton. What kind of man was he?"

She looks startled at the question. "Oh, it's not for me to say, sir. I hardly knew him, and he was the master. He was good enough, I guess, never yelled at me unless I deserved it. Is that what you want, sir?" ***Turn to 537.***

10

146

You thank Green for his help, and he seems relieved to be done talking with you. Lestrade consults his list, and tells Silversmith that you would like to ask him a few questions.

You study the butler for a moment. Silversmith is a large stout man, with the immense dignity and stuffy calm typical of an ideal butler. His very presence is a little awe-inspiring.

•*If you ask his account of the night of the murder, **turn to 470.***

•*Otherwise, **turn to 140.***

147

"Mr. Silversmith?" you ask, "were you privy to any of Mr. Milverton's business dealings, his work as an 'agent'? Do you know anyone who might have killed him because of business matters?"

The butler's chin tilts upward, and his eyes seem to glaze as he looks over you. "My master's business was hardly my concern," he says coldly. "We both preferred it that way."

Before you can ask anything further or change the subject, Lestrade cuts in. "But you must know that he blackmailed people," the policeman snaps. "Do you have an idea of the identity of his victims?"

"Sir, if I knew such a thing, I would be a criminal myself. I hardly think that a proper question, even for a policeman." You try to think of another line of questioning.

•*If you ask him about the other staff, **turn to 457.***

•*Otherwise, **turn to 166.***

148

"Did anyone assist you in your dealings with the villain?" you ask carefully.

Miss Miles sighs deeply. "No, I did not dare confide in anyone. I didn't know whom I could trust in so delicate a matter. Perhaps I was wrong—nothing could have made matters worse." ***Turn to 214.***

149

Stiff from bending over the tracks, you stand up and stretch. ***Turn to 371.***

150

You find it curious that Holmes apparently had an appointment with Milverton only a few days before his murder. There may have been more to Holmes' refusal to investigate than his distaste for Milverton's disreputable activities. ***Turn to 487.***

151

In studying the bay window, you find that one of the curtains is torn near its rings, as though it had been cast open quickly. You point it out to Lestrade, and tell him: "You see Inspector, the intuders must have hidden behind the curtain, and then dashed out so quickly that they tore the curtains as they threw them open."

"As they dashed out to shoot Milverton," Lestrade answers grimly. "He must have suddenly caught sight of them, and they killed him to gain the time to escape. Can you tell how long they were hidden here?"

You study the curtains and carpet and shake your head. "No, I'm afraid I cannot," you admit. *Check Clue CC.* ***Turn to 476.***

152

You almost wonder if your watch has stopped as you wait for ten o'clock, the time you can leave your lodgings. ***Pick a number:*** *(Add 2 to it if you placed an advertisement in 3 or more newspapers.)*

- *If 2-6,* ***turn to 159.***
- *If 7-12,* ***turn to 535.***

153

"Have you ever heard of a man named Milverton?" you ask, watching the men closely. "He was murdered recently." The two men exchange glances, questioning each other with their eyes. ***Pick a number*** *and add your Communication bonus:*

- *If 2-6,* ***turn to 143.***
- *If 7-12,* ***turn to 396.***

154

Milverton's dresser is a big piece of furniture, made of fine dark wood, carefully fitted and polished to a perfect shine. A cloth on top protects the surface from odds and ends — coins, a comb and brush, and other small things a man might throw down when changing. The drawers are well-stocked with a supply of quality clothing, all carefully folded and organized. A box in one drawer contains cufflinks and other items of jewelry. Nothing seems unusual. ***Pick a number*** *and add your Artifice bonus:*

- *If 2-8,* ***turn to 281.***
- *If 9-12,* ***turn to 541.***

155

"Can you tell what kind of gun was used?" you ask Dr. Gordon.

"Yes, at least in general," the doctor answers. "It was a small-caliber pistol, with a short barrel. I am not sure whether it was a revolver or an old-fashioned pepperbox pistol. Whatever was used was very light and not very accurate. The shots are scattered for the close range, and did not penetrate as heavier slugs would have. One or two of the shots would not have killed a stout man like Milverton, but six of them managed to do enough damage to finish him."

"A woman's gun, then?" Lestrade asks, and the doctor nods. "An odd gun for a man to use," the Inspector continues. "Well, perhaps they chose it because it could be easily hidden." *Check Clue H.* ***Turn to 191.***

156

Using Holmes' techniques you realize that Milverton's staff must have arrived in a desperate hurry. From the tracks you determine that some were in slippers and that others wore loose shoes, as though they had thrust their feet into them and run without taking the time to secure them.

5

Suddenly, you bend closer to the tracks, shaken by a startling discovery. Amidst the tarcks of the men, you find the marks of a woman's shoes leading in the opposite direction, heading towards the front gate. As the servant's tracks cover some of the woman's smaller marks, it is obvious that she left before they came running up, but the comparative condition of the tracks shows that there was little difference in time. *Check Clue AA.*

•*If you checked Clue A,* ***turn to 472.***
•*If you checked Decision 1,* ***turn to 602.***
•*Otherwise,* ***turn to 149.***

157

"The head wound?" Dr. Gordon asks, surprised. "Oh, that was nothing serious at all. It's just a scrape. He probably caught his head on the furniture when he fell. I shouldn't be concerned by it." You nod and straighten up from the body. ***Turn to 390.***

158

"Well, who's next, Inspector?" you ask Lestrade.

Lestrade replies, "Reynolds, the coachman. Do you wish to interview him?"

•*If you wish to see Reynolds,* ***turn to 282.***
•*Otherwise,* ***turn to 221.***

159

Finally you hear the clocks of the city striking ten. You wait a while longer, but there is still no response to your ad. ***Turn to 351.***

160

You have finished gathering evidence at Appledore Towers.

•*If you want confirmation of what the evidence means,* ***turn to 167.***

•*Otherwise,* ***turn to 247.***

161

Once you apply your mind to the problem, you remember that Escott was supposedly working for the gasworks when he first came to Appledore Towers. Someone at the gasworks might be able to tell you about Escott.

•*If you go to see the foreman at the gasworks,* ***turn to 258.***
•*Otherwise,* ***turn to 142.***

162

"What sort of man was Mr. Milverton?" you ask the page.

His face brightens. "Oh, he was a good master," he answers, "always laughing and enjoying himself. And he told Reynolds and Silversmith to let me ride as footman sometimes, so I would start to learn all different kinds of service to fit me better for whatever job I get when I'm grown. I saw some interesting places riding with him too, homes of toffs and all that. And one place more exciting." He seems eager for you to ask him more. Lestrade looks a little bored.

•*If you ask him what the exciting place was,* ***turn to 242.***
•*If you ask who might have killed Milverton,* ***turn to 424.***
•*Otherwise,* ***turn to 560.***

163

You try to order your thoughts on other clues while awaiting the response to your ad.

•*If you placed the notice in 1 or 2 newspapers,* ***turn to 360.***
•*If you used 3 or more newspapers,* ***turn to 362.***

164

"It will be a difficult case," Lestrade says, "for the victim was suspected of blackmail. There could be many people, some of them in the highest ranks of society, who will be delighted at his death. But let me give you the background of the case as we travel." ***Turn to 144.***

165

You examine the bay window. When the curtains are closed, the protuding window forms a small, hidden alcove. You examine the curtains, the window frame, and the carpet to see if you can find any evidence. ***Pick a number** and add your Observation bonus:*

- *If 2-5,* ***turn to 104.***
- *If 6-8,* ***turn to 151.***
- *If 9-12,* ***turn to 188.***

166

"We mean no offense, I assure you," you tell Silversmith. "No one suspects you of playing any part in illegal activity. You obviously are above such behaviour." The butler's stiff gaze softens a shade at your flattery.

- *If you ask him about the dog,* ***turn to 414.***
- *If you have no more questions for Silversmith,* ***turn to 268.***

167

You begin to consider just what you have learned from your investigation, and what other steps your conclusions dictate.

- *If you checked Deduction 5 and Clues G & D, or Deduction 3, Deduction 5 and Clue G,* ***turn to 618.***
- *If you checked Clues G & D, or Clue G & Deduction 3,* ***turn to 407.***
- *If you checked Deduction 5 and Clue D,* ***turn to 425.***
- *If you checked Deduction 5 and Clue G,* ***turn to 467.***
- *Otherwise,* ***turn to 286.***

168

"I see one thing," you tell the others. "The tracks here are faint, but someone obviously knew the house very well indeed. He led the way straight through the parlour without bumping into anything, then turned down the passage and went in to Mr. Milverton's study without a moment of hesitation. Now, let us see what the study will reveal." With a nod of agreement, Lestrade leads the way to the murder scene. *Check Deduction 7.* ***Turn to 356.***

169

You study your evidence and try to decide whether there is any more information to be found. You decide that there might be evidence in the houses of some of the suspects. You decide that you might be able to search one house without being caught.

On the other hand, if you get caught in the house of one of these rich and influential suspects, you will probably end up in jail for a long time. Inspector Lestrade would certainly stop you if he knew you were going to commit burglary to search for evidence.

- *If you search Miss Miles' house,* ***turn to 495.***
- *If you search Lady Sylvia Daniel's home,* ***turn to 500.***
- *If you search Lady Blakeney's,* ***turn to 342.***
- *If you decide not to search,* ***turn to 460.***

170

As you try to decide whom to visit and interview, you remember that Milverton's secretary, Jenkins, mentioned several possible victims of his master's blackmail. All of them are on your list.

- *If you only want to visit people mentioned by Jenkins,* ***turn to 454.***
- *If you want to visit every possible victim,* ***turn to 363.***

171

"You will be forced to talk to someone about this case," you say carefully. "Isn't it better to talk to me than to Inspector Lestrade? Remember that Lord Ellington assured you that I can be trusted." ***Pick a number*** *and add your Communication bonus:*

- *If 2-3,* ***turn to 120.***
- *If 4-12,* ***turn to 112.***

172

You learn nothing more of interest from the big safe. ***Turn to 193.***

173

"What was your opinion of Mr. Milverton?" you ask.

Shepherd hesitates, then answers. "He was a good enough master, sir. He never shouted if you did your work right, though if you did make a muck of things he had a hard edge to his tongue. But with Silversmith running the house, none of us had much chance to make a mess, sir, so the master were no problem. He paid good too. I wish we'd caught the blighters what killed him." ***Pick a number*** *and add your Intuition bonus:*

- *If 2-7,* ***turn to 213.***
- *If 8-12,* ***turn to 218.***

174

Milverton had an appointment with the Countess d'Albert's maid at midnight. Perhaps she killed Milverton and fled before the servants came. *Check Deduction 10.* ***Turn to 390.***

175

"The murdered man was named Charles Augustus Milverton," you say. "Have you heard of him? I have heard that he had dealings with many people of your social class."

"Milverton?" she answers, thoughtfully, "I can't say that I've heard of the fellow, or ever met him. How could his death have anything to do with me?" In answer, you try to explain tactfully that Milverton was a blackmailer who preyed on people like her. ***Pick a number*** *and add your Communications bonus: (Add 2 if you checked Decision 20.)*

- *If 2-8,* ***turn to 245.***
- *If 9-12,* ***turn to 107.***

8

176

As eager as you are to get on with the case, you must wait until ten o'clock to see if you receive a reply to your advertisement. You try to concentrate on the morning newspaper, but you find that you are not really reading it.

•*If you checked Clue V*, ***turn to 152.***
•*Otherwise*, ***turn to 378.***

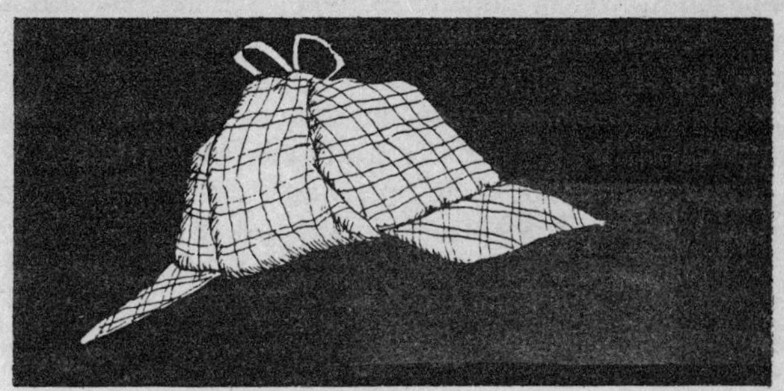

177

You check your notes from the interview to find where Escott lives, then take a hansom out to the neighborhood to pursue your inquiries. ***Pick a number*** *and add your Scholarship bonus:*

•*If 2-7*, ***turn to 209.***
•*If 8-12*, ***turn to 375.***

178

As you consider your next question, you realize you do not know much about the household routine at Appledore Towers.

•*If you ask Silversmith about it*, ***turn to 225.***
•*Otherwise*, ***turn to 134.***

179

The doctor looks surprised, then begins. "Very well, Holmes. You see, cousin, this villain Milverton was blackmailing one of Holmes' clients. Holmes and I were the two hidden men. We went to Appledore Towers to find and destroy the papers he used to threaten her. After Holmes opened the safe, but before he could find the proper papers, Milverton returned to his study. We hid, and some time later a beautiful woman came to see him. She had obtained an audience by pretending to have letters to sell him. Actually, she was a victim. Her husband, who was sick abed, died of shock when Milverton gave him some of her letters. If ever there were a justified murder, it was this one."

You spend a little more time with Holmes and Watson. Holmes promises to explain your withdrawal from the case to Lestrade. For you, this case is over. **THE END.**

180

"Lord Blakeney's death must have been a tragedy to your entire household, just as it was a shock to the whole nation," you say politely. "How did the tragedy occur?"

The butler's face shows emotion for the first time as he remembers the painful event. "It was heartbreaking sir," he says, "especially since we felt so helpless. Her Ladyship was attending the Queen at Canterbury when his Lordship was drenched by the rain while riding. He took to his bed with a severe cold that developed into pneumonia. He seemed to rally until he received a packet of papers in the mail. He read them and threw them into the fire. Then he wrote his wife a note. After that he seemed to give up all hope, surrendering to the disease. He was gone before her Ladyship could return." The butler seems on the verge of tears. ***Turn to 531.***

5

181

You travel to the townhouse of the Beavertons, and find that it is a three-story house facing one of London's small, elegant squares. Everything is as it should be, yet you do not see the visible signs of wealth that you associate with the nobility. When your knock on the door is answered by a butler, you ask to see Lord and Lady Beaverton, and give the butler your card and letters of introduction.

"It is impossible to see his Lordship," the butler answers, "as he has taken his schooner on a cruise to Gibralter. I shall see if her Ladyship has any time for you." You wait nervously until the butler returns, and feel relief as he silently shows you in to meet Lady Beaverton.

Her Ladyship is a plump little woman with white hair and sharp eyes. On your entrance she moves from her desk to a chair, and needs a cane to walk even that short distance. "An inquiry agent," she says, looking at your card, "I have never met such a person," she adds. "I hope your inquiries are not too personal."

You bow before speaking. "I wish to ask nothing unnecessarily personal or embarassing," you answer. "But I am trying to solve a murder and it is possible that you possess useful information in the matter."

"A murder," she says in surprise, "I doubt that I know a thing."

- *If you ask why she and her husband have separated,* ***turn to 451.***
- *If you ask if she heard of Milverton,* ***turn to 175.***

182

As you study the intruders' tracks, you see that they have begun to fade from the sun. It will not be easy to follow them across the heath. ***Pick a number*** *and add your Observation bonus:*

- *If 2-5,* ***turn to 491.***
- *If 6-8,* ***turn to 452.***
- *If 9-12,* ***turn to 276.***

183

You hide in the brush near Lady Blakeney's house, waiting for your helpers to earn their money. Suddenly, a voice behind you says: "That's the bloke, officer." Turning you see your helpers standing there with a bobbie. Both flight and combat are useless. You meekly accompany him to the police station at Cannon Row. ***Turn to 553.***

184

"You certainly were in a bad situation when you had to deal with Milverton," you say empathetically. "Even meeting such a man must have been a problem for a young lady. While one can never approve of murder, his demise has probably brought more happiness to people than many a nobler deed."

"It was a noble enough deed, to my mind," snaps Cousin Phillippa. "If the killer is ever arrested, the Queen should knight him." ***Pick a number*** *and add your Intuition bonus:*

- *If 2-6,* ***turn to 502.***
- *If 7-12,* ***turn to 186.***

185

You visit Lestrade. He greets you cheerfully and asks if you have made much progress. You give him a neutral answer, then say: "It occurred to me that it would be helpful to find out who might have been the recent victims of Milverton's blackmail. Do you have any idea whom he victimized?"

The detective shakes his head. "I have little time for gossip, but I have a friend, Mr. Osborne, who devotes much of his time to such matters. I consult him myself if I need such information." Lestrade writes you a note of introduction and gives you the address.

- *If you checked Deduction 16,* ***turn to 488.***
- *Otherwise,* ***turn to 250.***

186

It hardly seems possible that this young lady dealt with Milverton herself. You wonder if she asked someone else to deal with the blackmailer in her place.

- *If you ask her if she had such an agent,* ***turn to 236.***
- *Otherwise,* ***turn to 502.***

187

You wonder whether Holmes might offer some suggestion as to how you might identify the intruders.

•*If you ask Holmes' advice,* ***turn to 136.***
•*Otherwise,* ***turn to 277.***

188

In studying the bay window, you find that one of the curtains, at its rings, is torn, as though it had been opened quickly. You point this out to Lestrade, and tell him: "You see, Inspector, someone must have hidden behind the curtain, and then come out from behind it quickly, so quickly that he tore the curtains as he dashed out."

"As he dashed out to shoot Milverton," Lestrade answers grimly. "Milverton must have suddenly caught sight of them, and they killed him to gain the time to escape. Can you tell how long they were hidden here?"

You study the scene. "I think so," you answer slowly. "There are marks on the curtains showing that someone held them for a long time — the material was been crumpled and has not fully recovered. I would say there is almost no doubt that the two men hid behind the curtain for at least half an hour." *Check Clue G.* ***Turn to 476.***

189

"And did you see the two men, or do you think you can guess who they were?" you ask. As you ask, you wonder if you should have waited until the boy's puzzled look cleared and he was more settled in what he knew. ***Pick a number*** *and add your Communication bonus:*

•*If 2-6,* ***turn to 473.***
•*If 7-12,* ***turn to 418.***

190

Jenkins barely listens to your question before snapping: "If I had an idea who did this horrible deed, I would have told the constable who first answered our call for help. I do not know why someone killed him — Mr. Milverton was just a businessman." ***Turn to 421.***

191

You think over what Dr. Gordon has told you, and how it fits with your other evidence. ***Pick a number*** *and add your Intuition bonus:*

•*If 2-5,* ***turn to 390.***
•*If 6-12,* ***turn to 241.***

192

"I have no idea who killed him," Jenkins answers. "I did not know he had enemies who were that desperate." ***Turn to 421.***

193

From the safe, you cross the room to the door that leads onto the veranda. The key is in the lock on the outside, though the door is unlocked now. Silversmith tells you that when the staff returned from pursuing the intruders, they found the door locked from the outside. He opened it then to see what had happened to their master. You examine the door but you cannot tell if it was locked when the intruders entered the room.

You wonder what other secrets might be hidden in this study. You look at the big fireplace—could it hold a clue in this puzzling case?

•*If you examine the fireplace,* ***turn to 273.***
•*Otherwise,* ***turn to 529.***

194

You decide that Holmes and Watson might be amused by the page's wild story, and therefore go to Baker Street. Mrs. Hudson takes you up to the rooms shared by Holmes and Watson. Dr. Watson greets you warmly, though Holmes seems rather preoccupied with a book.

After a little talk about the news of the day, Watson asks: "How is your investigation going?"

"Well enough," you answer, "I spent the day at Appledore Towers interviewing the staff, and then trying to put all they told me into a logical pattern. A weary task, as Milverton had a dozen people working for him."

"So you have not solved the murder yet?" Holmes asks in a half- teasing tone. "But then, you had Lestrade's help; that would handicap anyone. Now, I am sure you came here because there was some point that you thought I might clarify. Tell me about it."

•*If you have Clue O,* ***turn to 599.***
•*Otherwise,* ***turn to 579.***

195

You try to decide what Mary Jones might know that can help solve the case.

•*If you ask her opinion of Milverton,* ***turn to 113.***
•*Otherwise,* ***turn to 326.***

196

The upstairs maid enters. She is a tiny woman nearing thirty, very plain and thin, obviously not too bright. "Just be calm, Bessie," you tell her, "and tell us what you saw and heard when Mr. Milverton was killed. But only what you saw and heard yourself."

"Yessir," she answers. "Well, I was in my bed asleep when it started, but the shots woke me up so's I heard the last two or three. Immediately all the men started yelling and jumping around, so I grabbed my robe and dashed out to see what it was all about. I followed the men down to Mr. Milverton's study, but they couldn't get in, so we all ran around outside. I followed a little behind them, and saw Tommy Green grab one of them as he were going over the wall, but the bloke kicked Tommy and got clean away. They were all scared to chase the men on over the 'eath, on account of their gun. Then I comes back to the 'ouse and goes back to bed. Couldn't sleep none, though, not with the master lying dead down there in the study."

•*If you ask her opinion of Milverton,* ***turn to 438.***
•*Otherwise,* ***turn to 610.***

197

"I don't know who locked away Brutus last night," the Butler replies. "When I went to tell one of the men, the job had already been done."

"But who was permitted to do it?" you continue.

The butler softens. "Well," he admits, "he is a difficult beast at times, and not many can tie him up when he's fresh. I'd say the only ones who could are Green, Yates, Mary Jones and Helen, the kitchenmaid who feeds him. All the others are scared to touch him." *Check Deduction 11.* ***Turn to 268.***

198

You consider the housemaid's comment that she was crying, and therefore didn't hear the gunshots.

- *If you ask why she was crying,* ***turn to 612.***
- *Otherwise,* ***turn to 195.***

199

"Do you have any idea who might have killed Mr. Milverton?" you ask. ***Turn to 190.***

200

"Why did you stop your pursuit at the wall?" you ask.

Silversmith looks surprised at the question. "It only seemed sensible, sir," he answers. "By the time the rest of us joined young Green, the men had a good start over the heath. None of us was dressed for a long run across the heath, cold as it was, and none of us liked the broken glass on top of the wall, nor the men's gun, once we had a moment to think about it. I felt we had to go and see to the master, to see if something could be done for him. We didn't know if he was alive or dead."

"So you returned to his study?" Lestrade asks.

"Yes, we did." ***Turn to 439.***

[11]

201

Miss Phillippa Blackwell leads you into a small drawing room and presents you to Lady Eva. The room is nicely furnished, but shows no signs of fabulous wealth. The Lady herself is short, blonde, under twenty, fresh-faced and pretty, but very nervous. She is wearing a simple but pretty blue dress. You wonder: does she have enough money to be a worthy target for blackmail?

After an exchange of polite greetings, you ask Lady Eva if she has been blackmailed by Milverton. While her cousin glares at you, the young lady hesitates, then nods. "He did try to blackmail me," she whispers. "He had some old letters of mine, and offered to sell them back to me for seven thousand pounds. I didn't know what to do. It may be terrible to say so, for his death was horrible, but it was a great relief to read that he had been killed, and to know that I was free of that threat."

•*If you ask if she paid Milverton,* ***turn to 554.***
•*Otherwise,* ***turn to 279.***

202

Convinced that there is nothing to be learned from it, you close the wardrobe. ***Turn to 403.***

203

Holmes studies you for a few moments before speaking. "You know that Watson and I were the intruders at Appledore Towers. Did we kill Milverton?"

•*If you checked Deduction 9 or Deduction 10,* ***turn to 499.***
•*Otherwise,* ***turn to 601.***

204

Holmes listens carefully to your explanation, then shakes his head. "You may have named the killer," he says, "but you have done it without gathering any of the evidence needed to prove the case. Your accusation is only a guess."

•*If you wish to investigate the case again,* ***turn to 490.***
•*Otherwise,* ***turn to 616.***

205

At first sight you think Mrs. Cox is the sort of woman you would like to have cooking for you. She is a red-faced, white-haired woman, very plump and cheerful, who obviously samples her own work regularly. She seems almost excited to be talking to you and Lestrade, especially when you ask her what she heard the night of the murder.

"I was lying in bed awake at the time," she says. "I was trying to decide whether my special ginger cake or a pie would be best for the next evening's dessert, when I heard them shots. There was five of them close together, bang, bang, bang, bang, bang, then a pause of a few seconds and one more bang. They was small sharp cracks, not a great booming noise like a shotgun. I got up then, and everyone was running around, but I didn't see nothing more, and Mr. Silversmith wouldn't let none of us go in to see Mr. Milverton as he lay there, poor soul."

•*If you ask her what she thought of her master,* ***turn to 329.***
•*If you have nothing more to ask her,* ***turn to 392.***

206

"Now, if Watson and I are innocent of murder," Holmes continues, "Who did kill Milverton?"

•*If you say you have no idea,* ***turn to 525.***
•*If you name the killer,* ***turn to 335.***

207

You wonder if she can tell you anything of use.

•*If you checked Deduction 11,* ***turn to 212.***
•*Otherwise,* ***turn to 394.***

208

Choosing your words carefully, you explain that in cooperation with Inspector Lestrade of Scotland Yard, you are investigating a case of blackmail. To build the case it is necessary to talk to anyone who might have been blackmailed. Due to the delicacy of such matters, Lestrade considered it wise for the unofficial officer to conduct this phase of the operation, so that irrelevant information could be hidden. Finally, you add: "And in such an investigation, gentlemen cut off financially by their relatives appear to be targets of such a schemer."

"Indeed?" John Patterson asks, "Well, it happens that we are no longer such targets for gossip. Our uncle has decided that we are not such evil young men and restored our income. That is why we are packing: we can move to better quarters again." You congratulate them on their good luck. ***Pick a number*** *and add your Intuition bonus:*

•*If 2-7,* ***turn to 105.***
•*If 8-12,* ***turn to 432.***

209

You wander the neighborhood and notice a street peddler selling flowers. While you consider buying one for your buttonhole, you tell him you're looking for an acquaintance; a plumber named Escott. *Deduct 2 pence from your money.*

•*If you cannot pay,* ***turn to 462.***

•*Otherwise,* ***pick a number*** *and add your Communication bonus:*

•*If 2-4,* ***turn to 462.***
•*If 5-8,* ***turn to 552.***
•*If 9-12,* ***turn to 266.***

210

"Yes, we realized that the dog had to be locked up," you reply. "Did you lock him up?"

"No, sir." Yates answers. "I don't do that overnight lessen the master or Mr. Silversmith tells me to lock 'im up. Likely was that little 'ussy Mary Jones what locked 'im up, so she could see one of 'er men friends. She and Mr. Milverton and Green was about the only other ones who would 'ave the nerve to put old Brutus away. 'e is somethin ' of a 'andful lessen 'e trusts you, you understand." ***Turn to 619.***

211

"I think that the two men the servants saw did not kill Milverton," you answer. Even Holmes looks interested. "In spite of the lateness of the hour, Milverton had an appointment with a woman. The evidence shows that the woman assaulted the man, if not with the gun, then at least with the heel of her shoe! I'd swear she killed him."

"My word, Holmes," Watson says in surprise. "You would almost think he was there watching, wouldn't you?"

"He is only applying my methods," Holmes replies coldly. "He must still identify the woman." ***Turn to 575.***

212

You remember that the housemaid was one of the people who could have locked up the watchdog.

•*If you ask her if she locked up the dog,* ***turn to 264.***

•*Otherwise,* ***turn to 394.***

213

You thank the footman for his help. He bows and leaves. ***Turn to 158.***

214

You thank Miss Miles for her help, and the maid shows you out. ***Turn to 239.***

215

You wonder if Helen could possibly know anything of use to your investigation.

•*If you ask her what she thought of Milverton,* ***turn to 145.***
•*Otherwise,* ***turn to 537.***

216

Leaving the desk, you glance around the study, wondering what to examine next.

•*If you look over the bookcase,* ***turn to 504.***
•*Otherwise,* ***turn to 478.***

217

"I think one of Milverton's servants killed him," you say. "That would help to explain the killer's quick escape and knowledge of the house and grounds."

Holmes stares at you in utter astonishment. "What an amazing deduction," he says slowly. "Even Watson would not have imagined that. There is neither evidence that any of his servants killed Milverton nor any reason why they would want to do so." ***Turn to 352.***

218

You realize that as footman, Shepherd probably rode on Milverton's carriage, and might know some of the people Milverton had visited recently.

•*If you ask him whom Milverton visited,* ***turn to 219.***
•*Otherwise,* ***turn to 213.***

219

"As footman," you begin, "you went out with Milverton to help with his carriage, didn't you?"

"Of course. That's my job," he replies.

"Do you remember any of the places he visited recently?" you ask.

"No sir, I don't," he answers stiffly. "It ain't none of my business to remember such things. In fact it's a part of my business not to remember. A man who don't remember his master's secrets can't tell them. I learned that when I was a bootboy ten years old, sir." Neither you nor Lestrade can get more out of him. You tell him he can go. He bows and leaves. ***Turn to 158.***

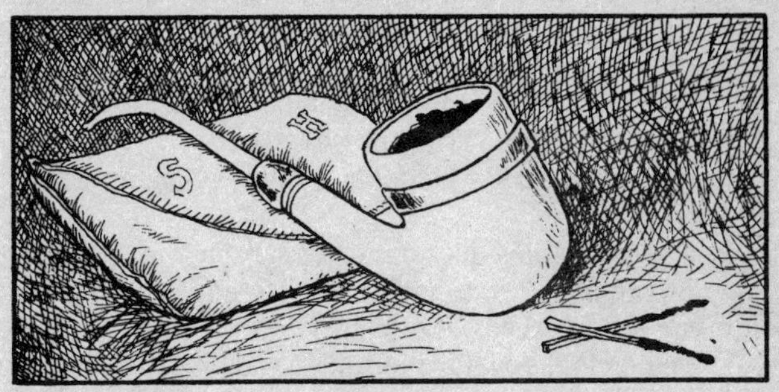

220

From the combination of evidence you have found, you are certain that a woman came to Milverton's rooms last night, in addition to the two men who were seen leaving. It is possible that the woman rather than the men killed the blackmailer. The case seems to grow more complex as you learn more. ***Turn to 247.***

221

Lestrade stands and stretches for a moment before consulting his list again. "Only a couple of the staff left, thank goodness," he says. "The Groom, Yates, is next on the list. Do you want to talk to him?"

•*If you talk to the groom,* ***turn to 431.***
•*Otherwise,* ***turn to 474.***

222

Once you have finished looking at the burglarized door, you open it and the butler leads you into the house. The heat and humidity of the greenhouse makes you dizzy for a moment, then Silversmith opens the door into the parlour. Lestrade and the butler stand aside while you examine the floor and furniture. You vaguely wonder how Milverton managed to fit so much furniture into the space. There seems to be an excess of tables and chairs. Every table and shelf in the place is filled with vases, ceramic figures and other bric-a-brac. The marks in the carpet are too indistinct to reveal anything. You move to the connecting passage and see that the footprints, faint though they are, lead straight to another door.

"What door is that?" you ask Silversmith.

"The door to Mr. Milverton's study," the butler answers stolidly.

You ponder further questions, then step back to the parlour. "Mr. Silversmith," you continue, "has any of the parlour furniture been pushed out of place?"

The butler looks over the furniture, and his face screws up. Then: "Everything seems to be as it should," he finally answers. "Certainly nothing has been knocked over or pushed far out of place." ***Pick a number*** *and add your Observation bonus:*

- *If 2-6,* ***turn to 345.***
- *If 7-12,* ***turn to 168.***

223

Once the page has left, closing the door behind him, you look over at Lestrade, smile, and ask, "What do you think of the lad's theory that our two intruders were Sherlock Holmes and Dr. Watson?"

Lestrade just shakes his head, seemingly at a loss for words. Finally, he says: "I have been a police officer in London for almost twenty years sir, and I don't think I have ever heard a more ridiculous theory."

"It was rather odd," you admit, "but is it totally absurd? Couldn't Mr. Holmes have had some business with this man Milverton?"

"No!" Lestrade answers sharply. "He refused to take the case because he felt that the killing might be justified, since Milverton's blackmail could not be countered by legal means. Feeling as he did, he would never have associated himself with Milverton.

"Might Holmes' stated position have been a cover for his connection?" you suggest. "The lad said the descriptions matched Holmes' and Watson's."

"And as Holmes said to me when I described the case to him, 'That's rather vague. It might be a description of Watson.' No sir, the boy's mind is filled with nonsense. Don't let it influence your investigation."

•*If you checked Deduction 6,* ***turn to 260.***
•*Otherwise,* ***turn to 244.***

224

"So you were the men," you say, surprised. "Could you tell me what you were doing there, Mr. Holmes? And why have you not informed Lestrade of the identity of the killer?"

Holmes answers curtly: "I am not required to do either your work or Lestrade's. Watson and I were there to destroy some papers that Milverton was using for blackmail. I suggest that you abandon the case at once."

•*If you agree to abandon the case,* ***turn to 263.***
•*Otherwise,* ***turn to 265.***

225

"Mr. Silversmith," you say, searching for the proper phrasing, "I think it would be most helpful if you could oblige us with a sketch of the routine of Mr. Milverton's household — what happens here on a daily basis."

The butler nods, on sure ground here. "Yes, sir, that's the sort of question that makes good sense to ask. Mr. Milverton demanded an orderly house, sir, with everything clean and polished, tasks accomplished on time, and the staff available if he needed them. In his business as an agent, he often travelled around London, sometimes on short notice, and he felt that an orderly home contributed to his efficiency.

2

"When he was home, he took his meals at the same time each day, and always ate well. He went to bed at ten-thirty every night of the year, and always slept soundly. He was a man one could not wake up until morning, whatever one tried. I always locked the house at ten o'clock, so that I could tell him of any problems before he retired."

"And what security arrangements did he have?" you ask. "Did he behave like a man afraid of anyone?"

"Afraid, sir? No sir, not Mr. Milverton. He was a cold, hard man if he had to be, though a good master to us. He kept a gun by his bed and another in his desk, in the event that burglars should try to force an entry. And of course he had the dog loosed in the grounds every night, and the broken glass atop the wall."

You make a note or two before asking: "If anyone wanted to get at his papers, could they have entered somehow during the day?"

"No sir," Silversmith answers. "Mr Jenkins, the master's secretary, always spent the day in the office, doing his work. He even took his lunch in there." You nod, a good picture of the household routine formed in your mind.

•*If you checked Clue D,* ***turn to 130.***
•*Otherwise,* ***turn to 134.***

226

You rack your brain, trying to think of what information the coachman might know. ***Pick a number*** *and add your Intuition bonus:*

•*If 2-7,* ***turn to 312.***
•*If 8-12,* ***turn to 376.***

227

You remember Lestrade talking of the burnt papers in the fireplace. Thinking about how long it takes for a big mass of paper to be fully consumed, you wonder why Jenkins didn't save the papers from the fire.

•*If you ask him why he let the papers burn,* ***turn to 391.***
•*Otherwise,* ***turn to 608.***

228

You find the Pattersons' address, and a hansom takes you to their small flat in Oxford Street. *Deduct 1 shilling from your Character Record.* Their landlady leads you up to see them, telling you that you are fortunate to catch them. "The gentlemen are leaving me soon, sir."

When admitted to their rooms you find them packing, though they are polite enough to you, and seem impressed by your credentials. The older brother, John, is tall and thin, while James is short and stocky. Both sport mustaches.

•*If you checked Clue W,* ***turn to 327.***
•*Otherwise,* ***turn to 419.***

229

You find nothing more of interest among the remains of the fire. ***Turn to 529.***

230

You consult your list and see that the brothers John and James Patterson are listed.

•*If you see them,* ***turn to 228.***
•*Otherwise,* ***turn to 374.***

231

"You drove Mr. Milverton when he went anywhere, didn't you?" you ask, and the coachman nods. "What sort of people did he visit?"

"Well, most of the folk he went to see were toffs," Reynolds answers. "Nobles and gentry and other rich folk. Of course, that's the sort of people that a wealthy man like Mr. Milverton goes to see, you understand." ***Pick a number*** *and add your Intuition bonus:*

•*If 2-6,* ***turn to 312.***
•*If 7-12,* ***turn to 399.***

232

Helen the kitchen maid comes in, curtsies awkwardly, and sits down. She is a skinny, uncoordinated little thing, perhaps fiften or sixteen, with stringy hair and a plain face. Your first impression is that she is not very clever.

"Well, Helen," you ask gently, "can you tell us what you saw and heard when Mr. Milverton was killed?"

"I would, sir," she says timidly, "but I don't really know anything I could tell. I was sleeping, when everyone woke me up with their yelling and fussing, but I was so scared I just hid under the covers until Mrs. Cox came and told me it was safe. She needed me to help her in the kitchen then."

•*If you ask who killed Milverton,* ***turn to 441.***
•*Otherwise,* ***turn to 215.***

233

"Escott," the foreman mutters, "Escott. Aye, I used him a time or two. He was a very good man, but he weren't around here for long, sir. His father took ill and he went home to Nottingham to care for him. I'm afraid I don't have an address or nothing, sir." ***Turn to 142.***

234

You wonder what sort of information the groom might be able to give to you, if any.

•*If you know who locked up the dog,* ***turn to 619.***
•*If you checked Decision 11,* ***turn to 285.***
•*Otherwise,* ***turn to 619.***

235

Deciding not to talk to Johnny, you wonder what to do next. ***Turn to 260.***

236

"Lady Eva," you say slowly, "I am surprised that a young lady of your gentle nature should have attempted to deal with such a villain as Milverton. Did someone serve as your representative?"

"Yes," she admits. "I asked a very intelligent and trustworthy man to help me. After the murder, he sent a note assuring me that I need not worry that anyone else might use the papers."

•*If you ask the identity of her representative,* ***turn to 295.***
•*If you are ready to leave,* ***turn to 502.***

237

"Your papers indicate that you came here to investigate something," Miss Miles says, interrupting the pleasantries. "How may I help you?"

"I have been asked to look quietly into the case of a blackmailer," you explain, "by talking to people who might have been victims of the villain. I can talk to you without any official record being made of the case."

"You are a few months late," she replies bitterly. "As you have guessed, blackmail led to the cancellation of my marriage, sir. A man obtained some indiscreet letters of mine, and demanded that I pay a huge sum if I wanted them back. I refused to pay, and he carried out his scheme. But fortunately some right-thinking citizen shot the devil a few days ago."

"That was Mr. Milverton?" you ask, and she nods.

•*If you ask if someone helped her deal with Milverton,* ***turn to148.***

•*If you thank her and leave,* ***turn to 214.***

238

Your examination of the door reveals nothing helpful, and you turn your attention to the big safe. ***Turn to 349.***

239

You wonder whether you should visit Colonel Dorking.

•*If you go to see him,* ***turn to 309.***
•*If not,* ***turn to 484.***

240

"That's a big dog," you comment, and Green agrees. "And I could see that he's trained as a watchdog. Who could tie him up?"

The undergardener pauses to think. "Now that Mr. Milverton is dead, there's not but three or four of us that could tie him up without a lot of noise and trouble."

"And who are they?" you ask.

"Oh, I'm one. Yates, the groom, and Mary Jones, the housemaid can always make the brute behave. And Helen, the kitchenmaid can manage him, because she feeds him. I'm not sure whether he'd let her lock him up." *Check Deduction 11.* ***Turn to 305.***

241

You bend over the body and look more closely at the injury on Milverton's forehead. "What do you make of this mark on his head, doctor?" you ask. "Is it possible that he was knocked out, then shot while he was unconscious?" ***Pick a number*** *and add your Observation bonus:*

•*If 2-7,* ***turn to 157.***
•*If 8-12,* ***turn to 372.***

242

"You say you went as Milverton's footman to some very exciting place," trying to be explicitly clear. "Where was that?"

The page looks embarassed. "Oh, I talk too much sir," he answers. "Mr. Reynolds and Mr. Silversmith are always trying to teach me that what the master does or where he goes ain't nobody else's business at all." You look hard at him as he hesitates, trying to will him to talk. Finally the page starts again. "I guess I can tell you gentlemen."

"Yes, indeed," you agree.

"Well, it was maybe two weeks ago or a little less, I was footman when he went out in the late afternoon, and he went to see several people. The last place we went was 221 Baker Street, so I figure he must have been visiting Mr. Sherlock Holmes, the great detective."

"Are you certain?" Lestrade asks, and the boy nods. The detective looks disgusted, then shrugs. *Check Clue O.*

•*If you ask the page who killed Milverton,* ***turn to 424.***
•*Otherwise,* ***turn to 560.***

243

"One of the Patterson brothers killed Milverton," you say, "probably in revenge for being blackmailed by him."

"No, no, the evidence hardly fits," Holmes replies. "Milverton did not reveal his information about them to anyone, and they have reconciled with their uncle. They no longer had any reason to kill him." ***Turn to 352.***

244

You realize that Lestrade was not honest with you at the beginning of the case. Holmes refused the case on grounds of principle, not because he was too busy to investigate. You wonder if you should have accepted the job, but it is too late to turn back now. *Check Deduction 6.* ***Turn to 260.***

245

"To put matters in plain language," you begin, "the late Mr. Milverton was a blackmailer. He preyed on people of your class who had secrets they did not wish revealed."

"And what would make you think that any blackmailer would consider me a target?" Your confidence begins to waver as you can plainly see the woman's face turning successively deeper shades of red. "I can see that there is no reason for us to continue this conversation. Good day." At a sign from her, the butler leads you out. ***Turn to 463.***

6

246

Mrs. Lindon comes in, with the quiet almost invisible movement of the well-trained servant, and stands waiting for your questions. She is a a medium-sized woman of middle years, very neat and trim, a person confident in her own competence.

"What did you see and hear when Mr. Milverton was killed?" you ask.

"I was awakened by the noise of the shots, and especially by the noise of the men dashing about. Naturally I did not follow them outside — I am hardly fitted for fighting armed killers. When Mr. Silversmith told me that the master was dead, I called the police, and made tea. I didn't see anything of the killers, and I was too scared to go in and see poor Mr. Milverton lying there dead. I'm sorry I can't help you more — these awful villains should be hanged, that they should."

•*If you ask her more about Milverton,* ***turn to 127.***

•*Otherwise,* ***turn to 585.***

247

You must decide what to do next. It seems logical to interview Milverton's staff now, and you ask Lestrade if that is possible.

"It certainly is," Lestrade answers. "I have given instructions for all of them to stay here until they are interviewed, whether it be this afternoon or tomorrow. Silversmith can find us a room in which to question them." The Inspector pulls out his watch and consults it. Time is flying by. "Dr. Gordon, the police surgeon, is supposed to examine the body this afternoon. If you wish to see the victim yourself, we should go now, and leave the questioning for tomorrow."

•*If you see the body,* ***turn to 409.***
•*If you begin questioning the staff,* ***turn to 132.***

248

"Well, that is the way of women," you say sagely, "the sudden decision with no warning to the poor men who must deal with them. Had anything upset her, to produce the final pressure that led her to leave?"

"Oh, no sir!" the butler answers. "She was not upset. In fact, she seemed finally to have accepted her fate, as if she had relieved much of the strain she felt, and needed the trip to remove the remainder."

You smile, and continue chatting. "What else had happened that would have produced her action?" ***Pick a number*** *and add your Communication bonus:*

•*If 2-7,* ***turn to 458.***
•*If 8-12,* ***turn to 119.***

249

Soon the cab comes up to the house. After thanking Silversmith for his consideration, you and Lestrade board it to ride back into the city. Lestrade drops you off, and you wonder whether you can learn anything this evening.

•*If you checked Decision 13,* ***turn to 576.***
•*Otherwise,* ***turn to 512.***

250

You go to the "Three Continent's Club," where Osborne spends much of his time. You are taken in to see Osborne as soon as you show Lestrade's note. He is an older man with a cheerful, intelligent face. He greets you warmly and fills you with information on the scandals of the aristocracy, also giving you a good lunch during his talk. From his information you build a list of Milverton's possible victims. You take notes on each of them from his rambling comments.

John and James Patterson — *Their uncle cut off their funds due to their wasteful habits.*

Lady Eva Blackwell — *scheduled to marry a very jealous man, the Earl of Devoncourt, within the week.*

Miss Miles and Colonel Dorking — *Marriage cancelled two days before the wedding, apparently because each of them had secrets the other couldn't accept.*

Lady Blakeney — *one of the most beautiful women in England, whose distinguished husband died rather suddenly.*

Lady Sylvia Daniels and the Honourable John Morris — *whose scheduled wedding was cancelled suddenly by his parents.*

Lord and Lady Beaverton — *who have lived apart for several weeks due to a scandal.*

Captain Grey — *who lost a highly desired appointment as attache to Lisbon due to gossip.*

You thank Mr. Osborne and return to your quarters for supper and bed, turning all the facts over in your head, wondering which of these people should be interviewed. *Check Clue T.* ***Turn to 620.***

251

"Could you tell us about your household routine," you say carefully. "Who took care of Mr. Milverton's rooms?"

Mrs. Lindon is still outraged. "My routine, you ask? My routine was just to keep his rooms clean and neat, just like the

rest of the house. Nothing to worry you, who probably never picked up anything after yourself in your life." Lestrade looks as if he wishes he'd never heard of this housekeeper.

You decide that it is time to continue your questioning with some other witness. ***Turn to 259.***

252

You listen as Holmes attempts to persuade you to drop the case, then regretfully shake your head. "I am sorry, Mr. Holmes," you say, "because you know I have the greatest respect for your judgment. However, I feel I must investigate the case until I learn who killed Milverton and why. Murder is murder after all, and should not be forgiven lightly. The woman might have been an accomplice of Milverton, who wished to conceal her own misdeeds, or he might have stumbled upon a secret more dangerous than the customary material of the blackmailer. And I still have the greatest curiosity about the identity of the two men who fled the scene. But as I promised, I shall not reveal my conclusions to Lestrade until I have discussed them with you."

- *If you ask for Holmes' advice about the woman,* ***turn to 413.***
- *Otherwise,* ***turn to 187.***

253

You look across at Lestrade, a little surprised. "This seems very odd," you say. "According to your theory, Milverton came in, surprised the intruders, and was shot by them. However, the evidence of his desk indicates that he sat here reading that long document, and the ash from the cigar shows he was here for some time."

"They expected to find him asleep," Lestrade suggests. "He usually turned in early. Instead the men walked in and found Milverton sitting at his desk. In their surprise, they shot him without thinking of the consequences."

"How was he dressed?" you ask.

"He was wearing trousers, a shirt, and a smoking jacket," the Inspector answers. "The intruders did not rouse him from bed unless he was calm enough to dress before coming out here to confront them." You consider Lestrade's conclusions, and ponder your next step. *Check Deduction 3.*

•*If you search inside the desk,* ***turn to 596.***
•*Otherwise,* ***turn to 216.***

254

After supper, you go to Baker Street to see Holmes and Watson. When Mrs. Hudson takes you to their rooms, Watson is writing and Holmes is reading. Watson greets you cheerfully; and Holmes looks you over carefully.

"This is not a social call," he tells Watson. "Our friend is full of a piece of information he considers important, and on top of that he is a little indignant. What have we done to arouse you, sir?" he finishes, though you have the feeling he knows already.

"I spoke to a man named Malone, today," you answer, "and I learned much of the life of a man named Escott, the plumber who arranged to have Milverton's dog locked up the night of the killing. I'd have though you might have told me!"

"If it were my secret that took me there, I would have told you," the detective answers quietly. "But there are times when we must observe the greatest discretion to avoid embarassment to a client. Watson and I entered Milverton's house that night, but only to destroy papers he was using to blackmail a young lady. While we hid in the study, a beautiful woman came in, another victim of Milverton's abuse. Although murder should rarely, if ever, be justified, she got the only revenge possible by shooting the villain dead. No, no, sir," he hurries on, waving away your questions. "I will not tell you her name. Watson and I agree that she had no other recourse against Milverton's crime."

"But murder!" you reply.

"What else could she do?" Holmes responds. "I urge you, give up this investigation. To prosecute would ruin her, and no one will be happy if you pursue it to a conclusion." *Check Clue P.*

•*If you agree to give up the case,* ***turn to 581.***
•*If you continue to investigate,* ***turn to 445.***

255

While you wait for the cab, a commissionaire arrives at a trot, bringing a packet for Lestrade. "What is it?" you ask, noticing the way he eagerly reads through it.

He looks up at your words and answers: "It's the surgeon's report on the body. Not much in it that we didn't know already. Six shots were fired into Milverton's chest at close range. A small caliber pistol was used for the killing—a gun someone could hide easily." *Check Clue H.* ***Turn to 249.***

256

You gather your courage and visit Lady Blakeney. A hansom takes you to one of the most exclusive neighborhoods in the city. *Deduct 2 shillings from your Character Record.* The Blakeney townhouse is a fine old building, blending wealth with taste in elegant proportions. A tall, thin butler answers to your knock and shows you to a small room while he asks your business.

"May I see Lady Blakeney?" you ask, giving him your credentials. "It is a matter of some importance."

"Be that as it may sir, your request is impossible," the butler answers. "Lady Blakeney is visiting her estates in Scotland."

"Scotland?" you ask, surprised.

"Yes, sir. As you undoubtedly know sir, Lord Blakeney died suddenly, and the grief of his death and all the attendant details quite exhausted her Ladyship. She has gone to the country for a rest."

•*If you ask what Lady Blakeney looks like,* ***turn to 469.***
•*Otherwise,* ***turn to 483.***

257

You remember the notation in Milverton's notebook that the Countess d'Albert's maid was to visit Milverton at midnight the night of the murder. Could the Countess know anything useful to your investigation?

•*If you visit the Countess,* ***turn to 115.***
•*Otherwise,* ***turn to 456.***

258

Suiting your actions to your thoughts, you ask directions and hurry around to the local gasworks. The gasworks is a huge brick building filled with pipes and other apparati. One of the workers takes you to the tiny office in one corner, where Mr. Malone, the foreman, watches over his men. You introduce yourself, and tell him that you are investigating the death of Mr. Milverton at Appledore Towers.

"Ah, a good man Mr. Milverton," he answers, "though we'd lost much of his business since he put in them electric lights. He just kept the gas hooked up for emergencies, in case something happened to his electric power. But I wouldn't know nothing about his murder, seeing as how me and the wife were sleeping snug at the time."

"Oh, I know that," you assure him, "and it's only a peripheral matter that concerns me today. You know how it is with a murder; one must account for every detail, or the judge will have one's hide when the case comes to court." His nod is only moderately reassuring. He seems a little bored with your talk. It occurs to you that a little money might make the time pass more easily for him.

•*If you offer him no money,* ***turn to 299.***
•*If you offer him 5 shillings,* ***turn to 300.***
•*If you offer him 10 shillings,* ***turn to 307.***
•*If you offer him 1 pound,* ***turn to 308.***

259

Relieved to be rid of her, you thank Mrs. Lindon for her help and watch her leave the room. ***Turn to 102.***

260

Relieved that the interviews are completed, you inform Silversmith. "Yes sir," he answers, "I thought that would be the case. I sent Green to fetch a cab for you gentlemen. He should be back with it shortly."

•*If you checked Decision 8,* ***turn to 249.***
•*Otherwise,* ***turn to 255.***

261

After a little polite conversation, you thank Colonel Dorking for his time and leave. ***Turn to 169.***

262

After a little more small-talk, you thank Holmes and Watson for their hospitality and return to your own quarters. Eventually you fall asleep.

In the morning, you rise and breakfast early, ready to pursue the case more fully. ***Turn to 410.***

263

Shocked at the intensity of Holmes' demand, you offer to abandon the case if he will tell you the facts.

•*If you try to solve the case again,* ***turn to the Prologue.***
•*If you want Holmes' explanation,* ***turn to 289.***

264

You look at Mary Jones for a few seconds, then ask, "Did you lock up the dog, Mary?"

She shakes her head, then nods, hesitates for a moment, and says, "Mr. Silversmith told me to do it, sir, on Mr. Milverton's orders. Green and Yates were busy with something else."

•*If you checked Clue I,* ***turn to 565.***
•*Otherwise,* ***turn to 306.***

265

"I do not think I should abandon the case," you tell Holmes, "not after I have promised Inspector Lestrade to help solve it. It would not be honest on my part."

Holmes frowns, then sighs. "Well, if you must...," he says after a moment's thought. "But I will extract one promise from you — if you solve the case, bring your solution to me before you take it to Lestrade."

You agree to Holmes' demand before you leave Baker Street and return to your own quarters. The next morning you rise early and breakfast quickly, in order to get to work the sooner. ***Turn to 410.***

266

"Escott?" the peddler says slowly, "No, I can't say as I know the fellow. I never have no call to deal with a plumber myself." He hesitates, then goes on. "But I'll tell you who might well know the fellow, sir. You go around to the gasworks and ask the foreman. Most of the plumbers work for the gasworks from time to time, the foreman will likely know the bloke. Now excuse me, sir, I think that lady would like some of me roses." He hurries off.

•*If you go to see the foreman,* ***turn to 258.***
•*Otherwise,* ***turn to 142.***

267

"Well," Holmes admits, "That is a connection, although not a strong piece of evidence to base such a deduction upon. You should have found more evidence before accusing anyone.

•*If you investigate the case further,* ***turn to 490.***
•*If you would like Holmes to explain fully,* ***turn to 584.***
•*Otherwise,* ***turn to 203.***

268

You decide that you have learned everything that you ever will from Silversmith. After thanking him for his time, you ask him to send in Mr. Jenkins, Milverton's secretary.

Mr. Jenkins is a short thin man, with a dried-out look, as befits a man who spends his days sitting in an office. You ask him what he saw and heard when Mr. Milverton was killed.

"I was awakened by the butler banging on my door, and shouting that he had heard shots from Mr. Milverton's study," Jenkins says, clearly distressed. "I dressed quickly and went with him and the others. When we couldn't get into the study from the passage, we ran outside. Two men were fleeing through the garden, and we weren't able to catch them. Mr. Silversmith and I returned to the study through the outside door. Mr. Milverton was dead, and I felt it best that we touch nothing until the police came."

•*If you checked Clue J,* ***turn to 626.***
•*Otherwise,* ***turn to 101.***

269

You begin your efforts by identifying the marks of each of the two men. You find that they wore rubber-soled shoes, and that the marks are not distinct enough to identify the men. You realize that one of them was tall with a long stride while the other was probably medium-sized, with a noticeably shorter stride. As you trace their path to the wall it becomes clear that the taller man was in front of the other man, since the shorter man's marks overlap the other's in a number of places. ***Turn to 594.***

270

"That explains why Mr. Milverton was sitting up late," you say." The document on his desk did not appear fascinating enough to hold his attention at that hour of the night." ***Turn to 318.***

271

The Pattersons smile. "Our fortunes were restored that evening," John says. "We dined with our uncle, and enjoyed ourselves so much that we spent the night. The next morning he restored our money, and our joy was doubled when we read of Milverton's demise in the papers." ***Turn to 449.***

272

"There is nothing more I can tell you!" the poor girl gasps. "You must believe me! There is nothing I can tell you about the murder!" She bursts into tears.

At the sight of her cousin's distress, Miss Phillippa steps between you and Lady Eva, glaring like a female tiger protecting her cub. "Get out of here!" she orders in a voice that freezes your blood. "Get out of here now you cruel, cruel man. You may have Milverton's papers yourself, for all I know, but if you try to use them to hurt my cousin, I shall kill you myself!" Unable to face her wrath, you hurriedly leave the flat. ***Turn to 370.***

273

You begin to examine the fireplace. The flames are out now, but from the remaining pieces of wood you can see that it must have been a big, fine fire at its best. Charred remains of the burnt papers rest in the fireplace. Scattered on the logs are bits of wax that must have come from some of the burned papers. You look through the ashes, but none of the papers is readable. ***Pick a number** and add your Scholarship bonus:*

- *If 2-6, **turn to 229.***
- *If 7-12, **turn to 401.***

274

"Good lord!" you gasp, "How did he ever hear such a thing about you? I should think that such a thing would be hushed up for her own sake, whatever the cause."

"Someone always tells such stories," Lieutenant Fraser mutters, "and sometimes they make the stories happen."

"Really?" you ask. ***Pick a number** and add your Communication bonus:*

- *If 2-7, **turn to 589.***
- *If 8-12, **turn to 625.***

275

"We read of Milverton's murder," James Patterson says.

"One of the most delightful stories I have ever seen," his brother adds. "It should be a comfort to anyone with an ounce of decency that he will never blackmail again. If you find his murderer tell us and we will set up a fund to defend him in court." His brother nods in agreement.

- *If you leave, **turn to 449.***
- *If you ask where they were on the night of the 13th, **turn to 590.***

276

From marks near the wall you can see that one man fell as he scaled it. You wonder if he hurt himself in the accident, but his steady stride across the heath proves that he suffered no injury. You are able to follow the tracks of the men all the way to a road on the far side of the heath. A line of fine houses faces the street.

Lestrade looks around, then nods almost to himself. "Even late at night they might well have hailed a cab here," he tells you. "They come this way often, bringing people home or collecting visitors leaving those houses." *Check Clue C.* ***Turn to 387.***

277

Your discussion of the murder concluded, you talk of other things for a while. Watson is very anxious about the increasing trouble with the Boers, and admits that he is pleased that this is one war he will miss.

"Wise of you, Watson," Holmes agrees. "They say the climate of southern Africa can be even more miserable than that of Afghanistan. But the world seems full of such troubles these days — even if we manage to settle the South African problem in a reasonable way, I fear that there will be no such solution in China. Trouble is to be brewing there as well."

Watson agrees, and the subject turns to literature, where Watson mourns the passing of Lewis Carroll, and the breakup of the partnership of Gilbert and Sullivan. "I say, Holmes," he adds, "do you think they might collaborate on one more piece?"

"Unlikely, Watson," he answers. "They have never liked each other very much. Their successes held them together, but since their last effort failed, they are likely to continue along their separate ways. We must be thankful for the work such men did do, rather than mourn what they might have done. Besides," he adds with a dry chuckle, "the fewer writers in the world, the more readers left for the fantasies you base on my work." Watson flushes in momentary anger, then laughs. After a little more talk, you bid them good evening and return to your own home. ***Turn to 311.***

278

It is a beautiful though cold morning. You eat your eggs, sausages and rolls quickly. You do not want to waste any time before beginning the day's work.

•*If you checked Decision 14,* ***turn to 378.***
•*If you checked Decision 15,* ***turn to 163.***
•*Otherwise,* ***turn to 351.***

279

"The blackguard certainly waited for the most deadly time to threaten you," you say, and she nods eagerly.

"It is too bad something wasn't done about him long ago," she says.

•*If you ask why she feels so free of anxiety,* ***turn to 109.***
•*Otherwise,* ***turn to 184.***

280

"Just why did you want to talk to us?" James Patterson asks after a couple minutes of polite chitchat. "We are rather busy, as you can see."

"I am investigating a murder," you reply. "The death of Mr. Charles Augustus Milverton of Hampstead Heath. A sticky case, for the man was a blackmailer and there are many who wanted him dead. Did you know him?" The two brothers glance at each other, though you can't read anything from their expressions. ***Pick a number*** *and add your Communication bonus: (Add 2 if you checked Decision 20.)*

•*If 2-7,* ***turn to 420.***
•*If 8-12,* ***turn to 426.***

281

You find nothing hidden in or under any of the clothing and close the dresser. ***Turn to 582.***

282

Reynolds is a tall, powerful, man. His clothes hang on him without the grace you noticed in house servants.

"Thank you for your time, Mr. Reynolds," you begin.

"I'm glad to do anything to catch the man who killed Mr. Milverton," Reynolds replies. "He was a good master."

"Can you tell us what you saw and heard at the time of the killing?" you ask.

"I can sir, though I doubt it will do much good. The shots woke me up. It took me a moment to realize what woke me, but then I jumped into my clothes and ran out of my room. Silversmith led us to the study, but we couldn't get in there. By the time we went out the front door and back around, the blokes who done it were running away. We tried our best and Green got a hand on one of them, but we couldn't catch them before they was over the wall and away. None of the others had any stomach for chasing armed men across the heath, and I can't say I fancied it myself. That's all I know."

•*If you ask his opinion of Milverton,* ***turn to 429.***
•*Otherwise,* ***turn to 226.***

283

As you think, you remember that a paper called the Hornet is notorious for its coverage of scandals. It also occurs to you that Inspector Lestrade might know something useful. *Check Deduction 16.*

•*If you go to see Lestrade,* ***turn to 185.***
•*If you visit the newspaper's offices,* ***turn to 383.***

284

You give the Countess the letter from Lord Ellington, which she reads. She says: "You must have done well to impress Ellington. He is less a fool than most of the nobility. But I think you are following a blind path, sir. I am virtually immune to blackmail. For blackmail to succeed, one must be sensitive to people's talk. I pay no attention to such nonsense. Milverton could not have damaged my relations with anyone for whom I care."

"I admit the idea surprises me," you reply. "But in Milverton's notebook, there was a note that your maid was coming to see him the night he was killed. Have you ever spoken to Milverton?" ***Pick a number*** *and add your Communication bonus:*

•*If 2-4,* ***turn to 100.***
•*If 5-12,* ***turn to 110.***

285

Yates is one of the ones who could have tied up Brutus.

•*If you ask him about the dog,* ***turn to 527.***
•*Otherwise,* ***turn to 619.***

11

286

You think through the evidence, then shake your head. You have not uncovered enough evidence to reach any conclusions about what happened last night. ***Turn to 247.***

287

You look at your watch again, wondering if the thing has stopped. It seems as if you have been waiting forever. ***Pick a number:*** *(Add 2 if you placed the advertisement in 3 or more newspapers.)*

- *If 2-6,* ***turn to 159.***
- *If 7-12,* ***turn to 304.***

288

Once you have dined, you sit in your room and consider the events of the day. Concerned that you have taken a case that Holmes refused, you decide to visit him and explain your decision.

You take a hansom to Baker Street, paying 2 shillings. *Deduct 2 shillings from your Character Record.* Mrs. Hudson shows you up to the rooms shared by Sherlock Holmes and Dr. Watson. At your knock Watson's voice invites you to enter.

"Good evening cousin," he says pleasantly. "What brings you to our — my, what's wrong?" he asks, seeing your tense face.

Holmes looks up from his book and studies you. "You are very tense," the detective says slowly. "You have come to see us quite suddenly, yet you hesitated to knock both downstairs and while you stood at our door. You have done something you fear will upset me, and you wish to explain."

You barely nod, as Watson erupts: "But Holmes, what could my good cousin possibly do that would upset us?"

Holmes thinks a moment, then sighs. "I fear that he saw Lestrade today, and Lestrade obtained his help in investigating the Milverton murder. Our friend believes that I refused to take the case out of sympathy for the killer, and while his conscience tells him he should warn me of his decision, his pride makes it difficult."

9

You smile half-heartedly. You find it unnerving that Holmes can see through you so completely, but this time his ability saved the the need for long explanations. Slowly you explain how Lestrade insisted that you investigate, that murder should never go unpunished.

Holmes listens. "Yes, I can see his viewpoint, even if I cannot agree in this matter. Milverton was such a loathsome creature that his removal amounts almost to a public service. But you are younger in this business than I am, and you must learn by experience that there are times when solving a case does more harm than failing to solve it."

"Sir?" you ask, a little puzzled still.

"Promise me," Holmes continues, "that if you uncover the solution, come to see me before you tell Lestrade. And if I, knowing all the facts, insist that the result remain secret, you will respect my decision. Agreed?" You agree to Holmes' demand. *Check Decision 13.*

•*If you checked Clue E or Clue O,* **turn to 353.**
•*Otherwise,* **turn to 293.**

289

"A reasonable agreement," Holmes answers. "I don't see the need to use names, but to put the matter briefly, Milverton blackmailed a lady in the highest level of society. When she refused to give in, Milverton sent the evidence of her flirtations to her husband, who was already ill; he died of grief when he read the materials. Although I have argued against murder in the past, I think the lady had a grievance against Mr. Milverton that the law could hardly heal." You solemnly agree, thank them, and leave Baker Street a little later. This case is over. **THE END.**

290

You run through the information you acquired at Appledore, and try to decide which pieces will point you towards the names of suspects.

•*If you checked Clue D,* **turn to 257.**
•*Otherwise,* **turn to 456.**

291

When you visit Lord Ellington, he greets you happily and is delighted to write you a letter of introduction. In it, he recommends you as a very intelligent investigator who also understands the need for tact and discretion. You thank him for his help and leave to visit the countess. *Check Decision 20.* ***Turn to 572.***

292

The carpet reveals grim evidence of the crime, as it is stained in several places with spots of Milverton's blood. You learn nothing else of interest. ***Turn to 623.***

293

"Have you made any progress in your investigation?" Watson asks, curious as always. "The papers mentioned that the servants almost caught two men who fled the scene. Have you been able to identify them?"

- *If you checked Deduction 10,* ***turn to 211.***
- *If you checked Deduction 9, but not Deduction 10,* ***turn to 332.***
- *Otherwise,* ***turn to 357.***

294

You think of nothing else to ask the butler. You thank him for his time and leave. ***Turn to 547.***

295

"Who was your representative?" you ask firmly.

Lady Eva hesitates, appears to think about it, then looks over at her cousin, who nods firmly. "Very well," Lady Eva finally says. "I shall tell you, if you promise not to tell my fiance." You nod. "Through the help of friends, I was able to engage the services of Mr. Sherlock Holmes. If Mr. Holmes tells me that I am safe from all of Milverton's villainous plans, I can trust him." *Check Clue X.* ***Turn to 333.***

296

Satisfied with your decision, you sit down and write out the advertisement, which reads:

Wanted, to settle a bet. Cabbie who picked up 2 gentlemen near Hampstead Heath after midnight on the 13th. 5s reward for useful information.

You add your address and request that the cabbie come before ten either of the next two mornings. You ask a Commissionaire to take the notices to the newspaper offices. *Check Decision 14.* ***Turn to 290.***

297

Satisfied with your decision, you sit down and write out the advertisement, which reads:

Wanted, to settle a bet, cabbie who picked up unusual fare near Hampstead Heath, after midnight on the 13th. 5s reward for useful information.

You add your address, and request that the cabbie come before ten either of the next two mornings. You ask a Commissionaire to take the notices to the newspaper offices on Fleet Street. *Check Decision 15.* ***Turn to 290.***

298

You move around carefully to the back of the house, certain that no one is in a position to see you. Ivy covers the walls, and it is easy to climb up to the window you have chosen. Clinging to the ivy, you try to release the catch and open the window. ***Pick a number*** *and add your Artifice Bonus:*

- *If 2-7,* ***turn to 368.***
- *If 8-12,* ***turn to 350.***

299

"Just what was this loose end you wanted me for?" the foreman asks. "I've little time to waste."

You nod in agreement. "I need to contact a man named Escott," you say, and notice the man's eyes narrow. "He is reported to be a plumber who did some work for you." ***Pick a number*** *and add your Communication bonus:*

- *If 2-7,* ***turn to 621.***
- *If 8-11,* ***turn to 233.***
- *If 12,* ***turn to 361.***

300

"Pardon me," you say suddenly. "I shouldn't waste the time of a busy man like yourself without some compensation." You slip him five shillings. Deduct the money from your Character Record. "Now Mr. Malone," you continue, "Tell me a little bit about a man named Escott, a plumber who did some work at Appledore Towers. I need to contact him." The foreman's face twists in thought. ***Pick a number*** *and add your Communication bonus:*

- *If 2-4,* ***turn to 621.***
- *If 5-8,* ***turn to 233.***
- *If 9-12,* ***turn to 361.***

2

301

You read a letter. It seems to have been written by a boastful rake about his relationship with the daughter of Sir Henry Oxford. One section especially catches your eye:

> *The silly girl even wrote me half a dozen letters. You might find them very amusing, considering her current engagement with Colonel Perkins. Perhaps I could arrange for them to pass into your hands if they would suit your fancy.*
>
> *HV*

As you read the note, you realize that Milverton's fancy would involve a generous gift to the writer — a man cautious enough to have signed the note with his initials rather than a name. And if Milverton had bought the letters, the bride-to-be might have paid dearly for her folly in writing them. You pass the note to Lestrade and mention your suspicions.

"Aye, you're likely right sir," he agrees. "This might be evidence of blackmail, but it's a little late to press that charge against Mr. Milverton." *Check Clue BB.* ***Turn to 216.***

302

"Where was I when Milverton was killed, you mean?" Dorking laughs. "Why, I can't remember. It might help you find who did the good deed. We can't have that, now can we? No, don't ask again, sir, for I will not say a thing." ***Turn to 261.***

303

"Tell us the solution," Holmes says. "We are eager to hear. Who were the two intruders at Appledore Towers?"

- *If you name the Patterson brothers,* ***turn to 561.***
- *If you name Colonel Dorking and his nephew,* ***turn to 532.***
- *If you name Holmes and Watson,* ***turn to 591.***
- *If you name Captain Gray and Lieutenant Fraser,* ***turn to 508.***
- *If you don't know,* ***turn to 567.***

304

About half past nine there is a knock at your door. When you answer a small thin man comes in, obviously a cab driver from his clothes and horsy smell. "Did you place the ad, sir, asking about strange passengers on the heath the other night?" he asks.

"Yes," you answer, "I did."

"I believe one of my fares was your party," he answers. "Leastways, it was a very odd sort of passenger for the place and time. It was well after midnight, and a lady waved to my cab. She was tall and slender, and from what I could see I'd say she had to be beautiful, though she was veiled and wore a long cloak. Her talk showed she was a toff of the toffs, sir, the very top of the heap."

"Did you know her, or remember where you took her?" you ask.

"No sir," he answers, "I can't remember exactly where I let her out. I've learned to forget such things sir—sometimes your fares prefer it, if it ain't the right house." You thank the man for his help and give him the money you promised. *Deduct 5 shillings from your Character Record. Check Clue S.* ***Turn to 385.***

305

You wonder if there is anything else useful that Green might tell you. ***Pick a number*** *and add your Intuition bonus:*

•*If 2-7,* ***turn to 146.***
•*If 8-12,* ***turn to 543.***

306

The housemaid seems a little nervous. You wonder if she's keeping some guilty secret. ***Pick a number*** *and add your Intuition bonus:*

•*If 2-7,* ***turn to 366.***
•*If 8-12,* ***turn to 563.***

307

"Pardon me," you say suddenly. "I shouldn't waste the time of a busy man like yourself without some compensation." You slip him ten shillings. Deduct the payment from your Character Record. "Now, Mr. Malone," you continue, "Could you tell me a little bit about a man named Escott, a plumber who did some work at Appledore Towers? I must contact him." The foreman's face twists in thought. ***Pick a number*** *and add your Communication bonus:*

- *If 2,* ***turn to 621.***
- *If 3-4,* ***turn to 233.***
- *If 5-12,* ***turn to 361.***

308

"Pardon me," you say suddenly. "I shouldn't waste the time of a busy man like yourself without some compensation." You slip him a pound.

The man stares at the money in shock for a moment, then to your surprise he throws it back at you. "No sir," he yells, "you wouldn't give me so much for any honest purpose, and I'll be no part of your crooked games! Now get out of here, or I'll have the law on you!" Faced with an impossible position, you hurriedly leave. ***Turn to 142.***

309

A hansom carries you to Colonel Dorking's house. *Deduct 1 shilling from your Character Record.* A valet shows you in to see Colonel Dorking. He is a solidly built, middle-aged man, with a neatly trimmed mustache. His nephew, a tall young man, is with him. They both carefully read your credentials. "What can I do for you, sir?" the Colonel asks politely.

"Did you ever deal with a man named Milverton?" you ask. "He was an agent until he was killed a few days ago." ***Pick a number*** *and add your Communication bonus: (Add 3 if you checked Decision 20.)*

- *If 2-7,* ***turn to 571.***
- *If 8-12,* ***turn to 501.***

310

The minutes of waiting pass slowly. ***Pick a number:***

- *If 2-4,* ***turn to 125.***
- *If 5-7,* ***turn to 535.***
- *if 8-12,* ***turn to 159.***

311

You rise early the next morning and eat hurriedly, eager to continue your investigation.

- *If you checked Decision 8,* ***turn to 437.***
- *Otherwise,* ***turn to 410.***

312

You can't think of anything else to ask the coachman. You thank him for his help, and he leaves. ***Turn to 221.***

313

The minutes of waiting pass slowly. ***Pick a number:***

- *If 2-3,* ***turn to 125.***
- *If 4-9,* ***turn to 535.***
- *If 10-12,* ***turn to 159.***

314

Mary Jones, the housemaid comes in. She's a pretty young woman in her twenties, and she smiles sweetly at you and Lestrade. After your question, she talks about what she heard when Milverton was killed. "I was crying, so I didn't really know what was going on until all the men began running around and yelling at each other to be quick, and something about gunshots. I didn't know what had happened or what to make of it until Mrs. Lindon took Helen, Bessie and me aside and told us Mr. Milverton had been shot dead, sir. Oh, it was terrible." ***Pick a number*** *and add your Observation bonus:*

- *If 2-6,* ***turn to 195.***
- *If 7-12,* ***turn to 198.***

315

You take a hansom to 221 Baker Street. *Deduct 2 shillings from your Character Record.* Mrs. Hudson shows you up to Holmes' rooms. Watson answers your knock with a cheery "Come in." Holmes is reading by the fireplace; Watson sits at his desk writing. When he sees you, Watson smiles and greets you warmly. "What good wind blows you here tonight?" he asks warmly.

Holmes looks up from across the room and quietly says: "Now really, Watson, that should be obvious from the manner in which he ran up the stair and knocked on the door. Our friend has a new and important case and has come to get my opinion of the evidence."

Watson looks at you and you nod. "You do save a lot of conversation Mr. Holmes," you laugh. "Mr. Lestrade asked me to assist him in the Milverton murder, as you were busy."

For a moment Holmes seems to frown. "So that is what Lestrade told you, is it?" he mutters. "Well, I knew Milverton's reputation as a particularly intelligent and malicious blackmailer, and I cannot say that his death is a tragedy for the realm."

"But murder must be investigated," you reply, a little shocked by his attitude. "It is for the courts to decide the justice of the matter."

"Perhaps," Holmes answers, "but I have known several occasions when I did more harm by catching a criminal than I would have done by allowing his escape. Tell us what you have learned. We are wasting time." *Check Decision 13.*

•*If you checked Clue E or Clue O,* ***turn to 353.***
•*Otherwise,* ***turn to 293.***

316

The cabbie thanks you when you give him his money. *Deduct 5 shillings from your Character record. Check Clue V.* ***Turn to 351.***

317

Holmes listens to your explanation, then says. "You have shown that we were there, I admit. You show that we had some connection to Milverton, and also gathered evidence that we were at Appledore Towers. Good work." ***Turn to 203.***

318

Wondering if there are other interesting appointments, you leaf quickly through the book, in spite of Lestrade's restlessness. ***Pick a number*** *and add your Observation bonus:*

•*If 2-7,* ***turn to 487.***
•*If 8-12,* ***turn to 324.***

319

You recognize that the pebbles from the decorative border of Milverton's driveway: therefore it seems that an outsider killed Milverton. None of the footprints of the two male intruders had any of the pebbles in them. Perhaps a third party killed the blackmailer.

•*If you Checked Clue D,* ***turn to 174.***
•*Otherwise,* ***turn to 390.***

320

You search Lady Blakeney's room. In a small drawer of her desk you find what you seek. It is obvious her ladyship trusts her servants. Lying under some papers is a dainty little revolver, the size used to kill Milverton, the spent cartridges still in it. Under it are two notes. One, initialled CAM, makes an appointment at Appledore Towers for midnight of the 13th, the night of the murder. The other is more touching, and you are a little ashamed to read it.

Dearest Mary,

When I served the Queen abroad, the one thought that carried me through every danger was the sure knowledge that you were loyally awaiting my return. Today, I received a packet of your letters that shows me how misplaced was my confidence. They showed you to be romantically involved with a Mr. Milverton of Appledore Towers. I do not know how to live with this knowledge, doubly troubling to receive when I am ill. I threw the evidence of your betrayal into the fire. Know that I shall always love you.

Blakeney

You consider this new evidence: its meaning becomes clear to you. *Check Clue Y.* You leave the note in its place and slip out a window, and try to climb down the ivy. ***Pick a number*** *and add your Athletics bonus:*

- *If 2-5,* ***turn to 546.***
- *If 6-12,* ***turn to 539.***

321

"Do you have any idea who could have locked up the dog last night?" The butler frowns. ***Pick a number*** *and add your Communication bonus.*

- *If 2-7,* ***turn to 544.***
- *If 8-12,* ***turn to 197.***

322

"Why did you let the papers burn?" you repeat.

"I didn't think we should touch anything until the police came," Jenkins says indignantly. "If we'd dashed over to the fire and pulled those things out, we might have destroyed important traces of Mr. Milverton's killers." You consider what to ask Mr. Jenkins next. ***Turn to 608.***

323

"Mrs. Cox," you ask, "could you tell us about any of the people Mr. Milverton had talked about lately? It might help us, if he'd heard something he shouldn't have."

The cook screws up her face in concentration, trying to separate Milverton's gossip from what she heard from others. Then she smiles. "Yes sir," she says, "I can remember some. One was this Lady Eva Blackwell, who's to be married this week. He said if the Earl she's marrying knew of her flirtations in the past, there wouldn't be no wedding, just like happened when Colonel Dorking and Miss Miles learned too much about each other. And when Lord Blakeney died so sudden, he said it was because his wife had encouraged flirtations with other men, though I don't know how any woman could have been untrue to such a famous and noble man. Then there was the case of Lady Sylvia Daniels—she was supposed to marry the Honourable John Morris but his parents stopped the match because of something they heard about her. I guess that's all I remember that I heard of just from the master, you understand." *Check Clue L.* ***Turn to 392.***

324

One appointment catches your eye. On the 5th, ten days ago, Milverton had an appointment at five in the evening; written below it is:

Then, 221-B Baker Street.

This you do not mention to Lestrade. *Check Clue E.*

•*If you checked Deduction 6,* ***turn to 150.***

•*Otherwise,* ***turn to 487.***

325

You make your way back to the veranda and look over the scene once more. You wonder if there is anything else outside that you need to look at.

•*If you checked Decision 1,* ***turn to 371.***
•*Otherwise,* ***turn to 129.***

326

You wonder what other information you might be able to get from the housemaid.

•*If you checked Deduction 11,* ***turn to 264.***
•*Otherwise,* ***turn to 306.***

327

You remember that the driver told you that he dropped the two men off in Oxford Street. You wonder how close it was to the Pattersons' flat, and how to ask them about it.

•*If you say you're investigating blackmail,* ***turn to 208.***
•*If you say you're investigating Milverton's murder,* ***turn to 280.***

328

"What kind of man is your fiance?" you ask her. "Is he a working man or a member of the gentry?"

"Gentry?" she answers, astonished. "You must be teasing me. I'm not silly enough to think that any of the gentry would have anything to do with me. He was a plumber, with a growing business. The gas company sent him to check the pipes here. He was older than me, tall, thin, with a big lovable mustache. And he smoked his pipe all the time, it seemed like. A very fine man, you know."

"Very fine," you agree. "What was his name?"

"His name was Escott, Charlie Escott. He came here from Norfolk. He lives in a village just outside the city," and she writes down an address. *Check Clue M.* ***Turn to 394.***

329

"What sort of a man was Mr. Milverton?" you ask her.

"Oh, he was the best master in the world, mister. He paid me better than any other cook in the neighborhood by far. He said that he wanted to have me there always because I cooked so good, and he was a man who enjoyed his food."

"Do you know anything about his business?" you ask.

"I'm not certain sir, it being none of my affair, but he was very good at it, because he started with nought but the brains in his head and ended with this big mansion and all the money he could ever want. I think he must have dealt with the high society folk a lot of the time, because he knew all sorts of gossip about them."

"Gossip?" you repeat, a little surprised.

"Well, yessir," she answers. "Maybe it was a little wicked of us, but you can guess how a self-made man like Mr. Milverton would be amused by the airs of the gentry. Many's the time he'd come back to the kitchen in the evening to see if I could find him a little snack, and we'd trade all sorts of stories. He heard some I didn't know, but I heard some from my friends in service with other folk. He'd tease me too, sometimes. If I'd heard something outrageous, he'd insist that I tell him who told me, just between the two of us." ***Pick a number*** *and add your Intuition bonus:*

•*If 2-7,* ***turn to 392.***

•*If 8-12,* ***turn to 323.***

330

You look around the room, wondering whether any secrets are hidden here. The big dresser with its many drawers catches your eye.

•*If you search the dresser,* ***turn to 154.***

•*Otherwise,* ***turn to 582.***

331

After hearing your explanation, Holmes says: "You have connected Watson and myself to the affair, though you missed much of the evidence. You could have done worse." ***Turn to 203.***

332

"I do not think tha the two men killed Milverton," you tell Watson. "I have evidence that a strange woman visited Appledore Towers at the time of the murder, a woman who was able to assault Milverton's forehead with her shoe, of all things. I think it maybe safe to assume that she could only have delivered the blow once Milverton was own. That could mark her as the killer.

"It certainly would," Watson agrees heartily.

An impressive deduction," the detective agrees. "It would be even more impressive if he were able to identify the woman."***Turn to 575.***

333

You exchange a few more polite words with Lady Eva and her cousin, thank them for their help, and leave the flat. ***Turn to 370.***

334

Mrs. Cox, Milverton's cook, spoke to you of the long talks she had with Milverton, during which he relayed spicy gossip. She mentioned several important people whom Milverton talked about: all of them are on your list of possible blackmail vicitms. You realize that you could save a lot of time by not visiting those she did not mention.

- *If you want to visit only people Mrs. Cox mentioned,* ***turn to 374.***
- *If you want to, visit all the possible suspects,* ***turn to 363.***

335

You draw a deep breath, ready to name the murderer, and hoping that you are not going to embarass yourself with a silly mistake.

- *If you name one the servants,* ***turn to 217.***
- *If you name Lady Eva Blackwell,* ***turn to 562.***
- *If you name Lady Blakeney,* ***turn to 453.***
- *If you name the Patterson brothers,* ***turn to 243.***
- *If you name Miss Miles,* ***turn to 114.***
- *If you name Colonel Dorking,* ***turn to 106.***
- *If you name Miss Phillippa Blackwell,* ***turn to 603.***

336

"Your story doesn't quite ring true," you mutter, trying to buy a little time.

"Well, I guess I made up the bag, sir," he admits, "but I took two toffs on into town very late that night, one tall, the other shorter, with a mustache. Never set eyes on either of them before." *Check Clue V.* ***Pick a number*** *and add your Observation bonus:*

- *If 2-7,* ***turn to 346.***
- *If 8-12,* ***turn to 348.***

337

Holmes appears irritated at the question. "Really!" he snaps, "I hardly consider that an appropriate question. I thought I had made it quite clear that I believe it would be for the best if no one discovered her identity." He consults his watch, then turns back to you. "Perhaps it would be best if you returned home. You will want to be fresh in the morning, when you resume your investigation." He then picks up his book and begins reading again. With a quick bow to Holmes and a word with Watson, you leave 221-B Baker Street. ***Turn to 311.***

338

"He's right, Holmes," Watson says through his laughter, "that is one of the silliest stories ever told within these walls."

"But is it true?" you ask suddenly, cutting through Watson's laughter. "Were you the men in Milverton's study?" ***Pick a number*** *and add your Communication bonus:*

- *If 2-6,* ***turn to 592.***
- *If 7-11,* ***turn to 545.***
- *If 12,* ***turn to 408.***

339

The wardrobe stands more than seven-feet high and is made from the same beautiful dark wood as the other furniture. The top is empty. Inside, it is filled with fine suits, evening and morning-wear, and other gentleman's clothing. Several pairs of shoes line the floor. ***Pick a number** and add your Intuition bonus:*

•*If 2-6,* ***turn to 202.***
•*If 7-12,* ***turn to 534.***

340

Using Holmes' techniques you realize that Milverton's staff arrived in a desperate hurry. From the tracks you determine that some were in slippers and that the rest wore loose shoes, as though they had thrust their feet into them and run without taking the time to secure them.

•*If you checked Decision 1,* ***turn to 602.***
•*Otherwise,* ***turn to 149.***

341

"Did you see anything else odd?" you ask.

"Yessir!" he says eagerly, "Just before them two men, there was a real pretty lady what got onto another bloke's cab. Real strange that was, mister, to see a lady out by herself after midnight." You thank the cabbie for his help and give him his reward. *Deduct 5 shillings from your Character Record.* ***Turn to 351.***

342

Determined to search Lady Blakeney's residence for evidence, you return to the neighborhood that evening. A fog is settling in, which should help you carry out your plan. You walk around the townhouse, studying the house and property. You know enough about this sort of house to guess accurately where her bedroom is located. Two courses of action appear suitable to you. You can get some people to create a disturbance. If this draws the servants out of the house, you can slip in and go upstairs. Your other choice would be to sneak in through an upstairs window.

•*If you create the disturbance,* ***turn to 514.***
•*If you sneak in by the window,* ***turn to 298.***
•*If you give up the burglary attempt,* ***turn to 460.***

343

"But, Mr. Jenkins," you ask in a surprised tone, "why allow the papers of such a business to be burned? I would think some of them might have been very valuable. After all, Mr. Milverton apparently kept them in his safe."

Jenkins hesitates before answering. "As I was saying, some of these transactions were accomplished very quietly. Mr. Milverton always promised that if a transaction failed, he would take care that the papers didn't fall into the wrong hands."

•*If you try to get more information,* ***turn to 464.***
•*Otherwise,* ***turn to 566.***

344

Lestrade tells you that Shepherd, the footman is next.

•*If you see Shepherd,* ***turn to 577.***
•*Otherwise,* ***turn to 158.***

345

"Well," you say to Lestrade, "There's nothing to be learned here about the intruders. We had better look over the murder scene now." The inspector nods in grim agreement and leads the way to Milverton's study. ***Turn to 356.***

346

The driver waits while you decide what to do.

•*If you thank him and pay him,* ***turn to 139.***
•*If you ask him if he knows anything else,* ***turn to 341.***

347

"You were so close to the intruders, Green," you say carefully, "I'm surprised that you did not follow them over the wall and across the heath."

He stares at you and laughs. "Have you looked at the top of the wall, sir?" he demands. "It's covered with broken glass, and I had nought but my shirt and thin trousers on. Besides, I did not want to follow them out on the open heath, not when I knew they had a gun and was willing to use it." ***Turn to 146.***

348

The driver waits while you decide what to do. Studying his face, you realize that he is really Sherlock Holmes, trying to fool you with one of his famous disguises.

- *If you thank and pay him,* ***turn to 139.***
- *If you say, "Thank you, Mr. Holmes,"* ***turn to 103.***
- *If you ask him if he knows anything else,* ***turn to 341.***

349

The safe is a tall strong unit, painted green, with brass knobs and hinges gleaming in the light. It is big enough to have held many papers, as well as money and securities. Even a glance shows that the door was forced open. Inside, you find that the compartments containing money and other valuables have not been disturbed, but sections designed for papers are empty. "Do you know if Mr. Milverton kept papers in here?" you ask Silversmith.

"Yes, sir," he answers. "He considered some of his business papers very confidential, and stored them there." ***Pick a number*** *and add your Scholarship bonus:*

- *If 2-8,* ***turn to 172.***
- *If 9-12,* ***turn to 355.***

350

Your guess was correct — you are obviously in the private rooms of Lady Blakeney. The furnishings are of the finest and most tasteful sort. You begin to search for anything of use in the case. ***Pick a number*** *and add your Artifice bonus.*

- *If 2-6,* ***turn to 122.***
- *If 7-12,* ***turn to 320.***

351

You leave your quarters, considering your next step as you do so.

- *If you checked Clue T,* ***turn to 385.***
- *Otherwise,* ***turn to 367.***

352

You consider your mistakes and try to decide how to investigate successfully in the future.

•*If you wish to investigate this case again,* ***turn to 490.***
•*If you ask Holmes for an explanation,* ***turn to 510.***

353

You consider that Milverton visited Baker Street little more than a week ago. You wonder what business Holmes had with a man he so obviously despised.

•*If you ask him,* ***turn to 446.***
•*Otherwise,* ***turn to 293.***

354

"You're a nice-looking girl," you say casually to the housemaid, and she smiles a little, half-shy, half-flirting. "Does your boyfriend ever come here to see you?"

She hesitates, then nods shyly. "Yessir, he does," she admits. "You see, I've just become engaged to a young man, and we walk out in the evening. He's such a smart young man. But I'm afraid that this murder might scare him away forever. He was supposed to come by the night Mr. Milverton was killed, and didn't, and I haven't had a word from him, not a word."

"I'm surprised he would be scared by a murder," you reply, "when he wasn't scared by that brute of a dog that you have here. But if he is, I'm sure that someone else will replace him."

The housemaid had frowned a little at your mention of the dog, but smiles at your last comment. "Oh yessir," she says cheerfully, "I was going with the butcher before I met my fiance, and I know he wants me back."

•*If you ask if she locked up the dog for her boyfriend,* ***turn to 443.***
•*Otherwise,* ***turn to 394.***

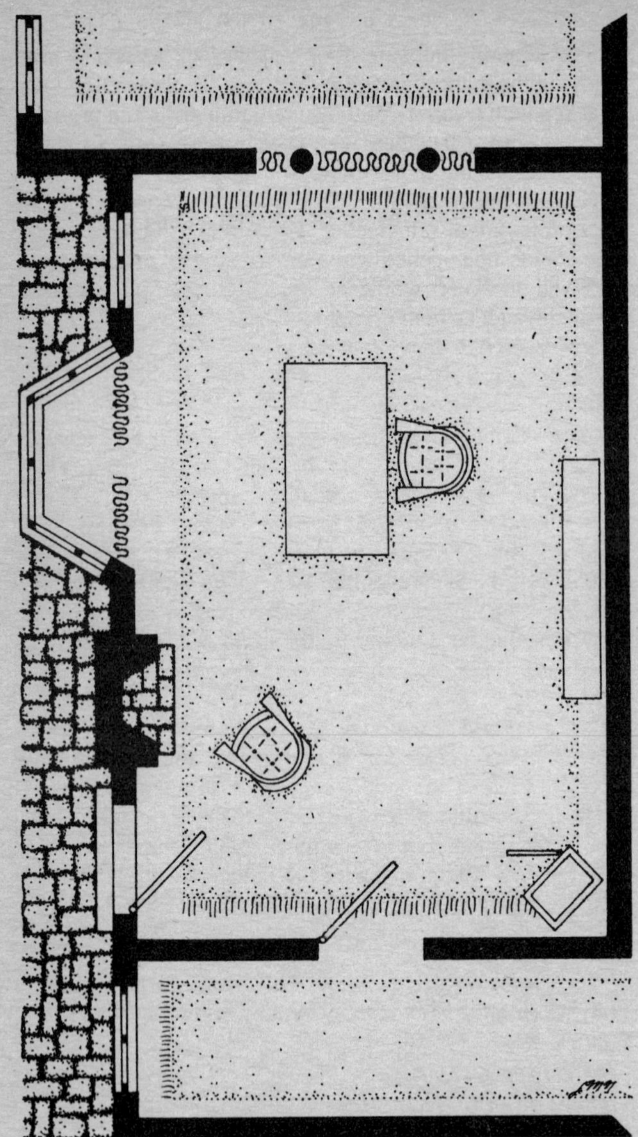

10

355

You examine the safe door and its lock a second time, studying the marks carefully. You can see that the safe was attacked with a variety of tools including drills and probably skeleton keys. All of them were used in a very skilled manner. You point this out to Lestrade.

He nods in agreement. "The man who opened this had to be a professional safecracker," he agrees. "Otherwise, the safe couldn't be opened without the key or explosives."

"Even an expert would need time to open it," you say, "probably half an hour or more," and Lestrade agrees. *Check Deduction 5.*

•*If you checked Deduction 3,* ***turn to 422.***
•*Otherwise,* ***turn to 193.***

356

Lestrade opens the door and turns on the electric light. In its glare you look over the room where a man died the night before. The study is a medium-sized room, comfortably furnished. You guess that the curtained doorway across from you leads to the bedroom. A door in the outer wall leads to the veranda. A large fireplace is next to the door, and partially-opened curtains beyond the fireplace reveal the alcove formed by a bay window. In the center room stands a large, flat-topped desk with a turning-chair of red leather. A bookcase rests against one wall, while a tall, green safe stands in one corner; its door open.

"Where was the body?" you ask Lestrade.

"Milverton lay in the middle of the room," the detective answers, pointing to the exact spot. "The one door leads outside, while the portiere leads to his bedroom. We have not touched the safe or the desk, except to note that the safe was almost empty."

You begin to search the room, studying the carpet where the body was found. ***Pick a number*** *and add your Observation bonus:*

•*If 2-7,* ***turn to 292.***
•*If 8-12,* ***turn to 402.***

357

You explain what you learned at Appledore Towers to Holmes and Watson, flattered by the rapt attention they pay to your comments. ***Turn to 485.***

358

"You must have done it," you say, swallowing hard.

Holmes glances at Watson. "And why," he asks, "did we kill the man? Did we have good reason to commit murder?"

"This is what must have happened," you begin. "You went to Appledore to destroy Milverton's blackmail material. He caught you, and was about to kill you. Watson then shot Milverton to save your life."

"A good explanation," Holmes says, "and one fitted to Watson's oft-proven loyalty. Of course it's wrong," he adds, and you see Watson smile.

"Wrong?" you reply.

"Wrong," Holmes continues. "Watson's service revolver would make a much bigger wound than the tiny gun that was used to kill Milverton and wouldn't need six shots to kill a man. The shots were fired at close range into Milverton's chest—that doesn't fit your scenario." ***Turn to 206.***

359

You begin to examine the tracks of the servants as they ran towards the study from the outside. *Check Decision 1.* ***Pick a number*** *and add your Observation bonus: (Add 2 if you checked Clue A.)*

- *If 2-6,* ***turn to 340.***
- *If 7-12,* ***turn to 156.***

360

You try to match Holmes' exemplary patience while waiting for a response to your ad. ***Pick a number:***

- *If 2-6,* ***turn to 159.***
- *If 7-9,* ***turn to 137.***
- *If 10-12,* ***turn to 535.***

361

The foreman mutters the name Escott a time or two, then looks very closely at you, thinks again, and finally speaks. "Well, sir," he says, "I do not know a man named Escott, but I know a man who paid me to introduce him under the name."

"What do you mean?" you demand, trying to keep the eagerness out of your voice.

"Well, that weren't his name, sir, not really. He needed to learn a little about Appledore Towers on the quiet, and seeing who he was, I knew it was all right."

"Who was he?" you ask, and this time there is no hiding your eagerness.

"Why, it were Mr. Sherlock Holmes, the great detective," he answers. Thanking the foreman for his help, you return to your lodgings for supper, as it is past sundown. Eagerly you turn the information over in your mind, wondering just what it means. *Check Clue Q.*

- *If you checked Clue P,* ***turn to 411.***
- *Otherwise,* ***turn to 254.***

362

You try to match Holmes' exemplary patience while waiting for a response to your ad. ***Pick a number:***

- *If 2-4,* ***turn to 159.***
- *If 5-9,* ***turn to 137.***
- *If 10-12,* ***turn to 535.***

363

You doublecheck your list, making certain that you have all the names and addresses written accurately. The first name on the list is that of Lord and Lady Beaverton.

- *If you visit them,* ***turn to 181.***
- *Otherwise,* ***turn to 463.***

364

"Have you heard of a man named Milverton?" you ask.

"Milverton!" she cries, "I have never heard such happy news as when the newsboys cried the story of his death. The devil prevented my marriage. I only wish I had had the courage to deal with him as someone else has."

"So he blackmailed you?" you ask. She confirms this somewhat hesitantly.

- *If you ask if someone helped her deal with Milverton,* ***turn to 148.***
- *If you thank her and leave,* ***turn to 214.***

365

The cabbie screws his face up in thought, then nods. "You look like you can be trusted," he answers. "Now, he's a good man so don't you give him no trouble on account of me." You quickly reassure the cabbie of your peaceful intent. "Well," he finally says, "the shorter bloke was a doctor, Dr. Watson, who had a practice in Kensington. He fixed up a mate of mine who got kicked by his nag, and didn't charge nothing. Thank you, sir," he says when you give him the promised reward. *Deduct 5 shillings from your Character Record. Check Clue R.* ***Turn to 351.***

366

As you chat with her a while longer, you can see that the housemaid is very nervous.

- *If you ask her why she's nervous,* ***turn to 475.***
- *Otherwise,* ***turn to 394.***

367

Obviously, you must learn the names of some of Milverton's blackmail victims. Perhaps one of them will point you to the killer. You wonder how to go about it. ***Pick a number*** *and add your Scholarship bonus:*

- *If 2-7,* ***turn to 496.***
- *If 8-12,* ***turn to 283.***

368

As you carefully try to force the catch on the window, you slip and smash a pane of glass. The noise shocks you so that you almost fall. You hurriedly descend the ivy and vault over the back fence—noises from the house indicate that you don't have much time to get away. As you run down the lane behind the house, a whistle alerts you to the pursuit of a police constable. ***Pick a number** and add your Athletics bonus:*

•*If 2-6,* ***turn to 517.***
•*If 7-12,* ***turn to 515.***

369

You cannot think of any useful alternative methods to approach the suspects.

•*If you checked Decision 20,* ***turn to 388.***
•*Otherwise,* ***turn to 386.***

370

You consider the next n ame on your list of suspects: Lady Blakeney, widow of the late Lord Harold Blakeney. You wonder whether you should go to see her at all. Her husband has died only recently. All England considered him to be one of the bravest and most-loved men in the country, successful as a General, as the Queen's representative in several delicate matters, and as a Governor-General.

Lady Blakeney is a famed beauty, daughter of a country squire, and a familiar figure in all the best circles in London. It is said that she could choose from a hundred of the most eligible men in the land at any time.

•*If you see her,* ***turn to 256.***
•*Otherwise,* ***turn to 547.***

7

371

Once more you look over the grounds, then nod, satisfied. You have checked everything outside that you think could provide you with a clue. When you tell Lestrade this, he smiles and nods grimly, and asks Silversmith to join you.

"Well," he says, "you will find much more inside to catch your eye. Come around to this side of the house," he adds, leading you around a corner. "We will enter along the route used by the intruders." Lestrade leads you to a greenhouse. There is a hole cut in the glass of the greenhouse door, just above the lock.

"Where does that door lead?" you ask Silversmith.

"The greenhouse is attached to a parlour," he explains. "A passage on the other side of the parlour leads to Mr. Milverton's study and bedroom." You thank him and look more closely at the burglarized door. ***Pick a number*** *and add your Scholarship bonus:*

•*If 2-6,* ***turn to 492.***
•*If 7-12,* ***turn to 450.***

372

"The head wound?" Doctor Gordon answers, surprised. "That's nothing important sir, just a scrape. He probably banged into the furniture or hit it on the carpet when he fell."

Not persuaded, you see something in the scrape and ask the doctor to clean it. He picks up some tweezers and a cloth and cleans it out carefully. You find one or two small coloured pebbles, and a flake of leather.

"Why, that's a bit of shoe leather," the doctor mutters in surprise. "That's a strange thing to find in a head wound. It would seem that the killer ground his heel into the wound after he shot Milverton Well, we knew already that the killer was not fond of Mr. Milverton."

•*If you checked Clues A and B,* ***turn to 564.***
•*If you checked Clue A but not B,* ***turn to 319.***
•*Otherwise,* ***turn to 390.***

6

373

As you examine the door to the passage, you note that the lock has been strained, as though someone in the passage tried to force the door when it was locked. However, when you point this out to Lestrade and Silversmith, the butler has a ready explanation.

"That would be our doing, I believe," he says. "After we heard the shots last night, we ran to help the master, but the villains had locked the door from the inside. In the narrow passage we could not gain the leverage to force it open, and we strained it a little." Satisfied that there is nothing more to learn here, you turn to Milverton's big safe. ***Turn to 349.***

374

A prominent name on your list is Lady Eva Blackwell. You realize that a great deal of tact is necessary when an investigation takes you to the home of an aristocrat preparing for her wedding. She lives in the fashionable neighborhood of St. John's Wood. You go to the neighborhood and study the house where she maintains a flat. While she is not indigent, she also is not inordinately wealthy.

At the door you are met by a house servant.

•*If you ask to see Lady Eva,* ***turn to 459.***
•*If you send in a note for her,* ***turn to 436.***
•*If you decide not to see her,* ***turn to 370.***

375

You go to the post office there and ask to see a local directory, in order to find Escott's address. Looking through it, you find no one of that name. ***Turn to 209.***

376

You realize that Reynolds must have driven Milverton often when he went to see the victims of his schemes. You wonder if he would tell you who Milverton visited recently.

•*If you ask him,* ***turn to 231.***
•*Otherwise,* ***turn to 312.***

377

You go through the portiere and enter Milverton's bedroom. It reflects the fact that Milverton was a wealthy man who was accustomed to living in comfort. There is a large bed with a small table beside it, a big dresser and an even larger wardrobe. Several comfortable chairs complete the furnishings. The carpet and curtains are made of the finest fabrics, and the logs in the big fireplace are ready for lighting. You approach the bed. ***Pick a number*** *and add your Observation bonus:*

- *If 2-6,* ***turn to 593.***
- *If 7-12,* ***turn to 423.***

378

You try to put your other clues together while you wait to see if a driver replies to your ad.

- *If you placed the notice in 1 or 2 newspapers,* ***turn to 310.***
- *If you used 3 or more newspapers,* ***turn to 313.***

379

"I wish no scandal," you begin slowly, "but I am looking into matters related to the death of a blackmailer. It is absolutely necessary that I see everyone who might have been among his victims."

"Blackmailer!" Miss Phillippa snaps. "You sound like a blackmailer yourself, trying to frighten us with thoughts of scandal so close to the wedding. Leave now!" As she says this, she reaches for a nearby vase; a discreet and rapid exit seems the best course of action. ***Turn to 370.***

380

As soon as the idea occurs to you, you know it is a good one. You get a hansom to take you to Lord Ellington's townhouse, where the butler quickly leads you in to his Lordship. "A letter of recommendation?" the peer replies to your request, "Why, I'd write you ten letters of recommendation, my lad! Just a moment." He fusses with pen and paper for a moment, then gives you the letter:

To whom it may concern:

The bearer of this note is a young man of sense and discretion, whom I would trust fully with the most delicate information. You may rest assured that he will not expose facts unnecessary to the prosecution of this matter.

Ellington

You thank Lord Ellington for his help and return to your work. *Check Decision 20.* ***Turn to 386.***

381

Trying to remember every bit of advice that Sherlock Holmes has ever given you on the art of tracking, you begin to trace the path of the two suspects in the frosty grass. ***Pick a number*** *and add your Scholarship bonus:*

- *If 2-4,* ***turn to 605.***
- *If 5-9,* ***turn to 269.***
- *If 10-12,* ***turn to 613.***

382

You circle the wall that surrounds the estate, but you find that the glass was not disturbed at any other point. The intruders must have slipped in quietly at the gate. *Check Decision 2.*

- *If you follow the intruders' across the heath,* ***turn to 455.***
- *If you return to the house,* ***turn to 398.***

383

You go to the offices of the Hornet and convince them to let you go through their recent back files. Slowly you build a list of possible victims, though you wish they were a little less circumspect in their comments. You note two weddings that were cancelled suddenly, that of Miss Dorking to Colonel Miles and that of Lady Sylvia Daniels to the Honourable John Morris. John and James Patterson were cut off financially by an uncle, while Lord and Lady Beaverton have lived apart for several weeks. A Captain Grey had an important appointment cancelled recently, and the account of the recent death of Lord Blakeney sounds odd to you. Finally, the upcoming wedding of Lady Eva Blackwell to the Earl of Devoncourt sounds like the perfect target for a blackmailer, as there is evidence that the Earl is very jealous.

7

After thanking the editor of the paper for his help, you tip the clerk who showed you how the papers were organized. *Deduct 1 shilling from your Character Record.* You return to your lodgings and eat supper. As you prepare for bed you are still turning clues over in your mind, trying to decide whom to visit. *Check Clue T.* ***Turn to 620.***

384

You thank Helen for answering your questions. The little kitchenmaid was so nervous you're glad to be rid of her before she falls into hysterics. ***Turn to 624.***

385

You adjust your clothes and prepare to visit the possible suspects in the killing of Charles Augustus Milverton. Carefully, you think of ways to convince these people, most of them wealthy and prestigious, that they should talk to you about some very delicate matters. You have a letter of introduction from Lestrade describing you as an unofficial representative of the police, employed because of the delicacy of a current case. That will get you into people's homes, but it may not convince them to talk. Obviously, you can follow Lestrade's advice and suggest that it is better to talk with an unofficial investigator than to the police. But perhaps you can do something that will induce cooperation from these victims of scandal. ***Pick a number*** *and add your Intuition bonus:*

- *If 2-5,* ***turn to 369.***
- *If 6-12,* ***turn to 628.***

386

Though you have settled upon your tactics, you still must decide which of the possible suspects you will visit. You do not wish to unnecessarily trouble a member of the nobility or other wealthy and influential people. Which suspects seem most likely to be connected to the case?

- *If you have checked Clues K and L,* ***turn to 540.***
- *If you checked Clue K but not Clue L,* ***turn to 170.***
- *If you checked Clue L but not Clue K,* ***turn to 334.***
- *Otherwise,* ***turn to 363.***

387

You decide you have found everything you could by studying the intruders' trail across the heath. With Lestrade accompanying you, you return to the gate and re-enter the grounds to continue your investigation.

•*If you checked Decision 2,* ***turn to 325.***
•*Otherwise,* ***turn to 506.***

388

You remember the letter you obtained from Lord Ellington before you visited the Countess d'Albert. It should prove useful in gaining answers from others of the aristocracy. ***Turn to 386.***

389

Advertisements should stand a good chance of attracting the driver who picked up the intruders. You consider the proper text for the advertisement. Obviously, you will include the time and location where the two men caught the cab. However, you are unsure about the remaining text of the notice. Should you ask specifically about the two men, or should you ask about unusual passengers?

•*If you ask about the two men,* ***turn to 296.***
•*If you ask about unusal passengers,* ***turn to 297.***

390

As you walk away from the body, the attendants cover it with a sheet and take it away. You leave with Lestrade, relieved to escape the the grim atmosphere of the morgue. Lestrade consults his watch, then says: "It's too late to return to Appledore Towers and interview the staff tonight. I shall pick you up at your lodgings in the morning, if that suits you." You agree. Lestrade strides off towards his office at Scotland Yard and you return to your lodgings, hungry for your supper.

•*If you checked Deduction 6,* ***turn to 288.***
•*Otherwise,* ***turn to 556.***

6

391

"Why did you let the papers in the fireplace burn?" you ask. "They might have pointed to Mr. Milverton's killer." Jenkins trembles a bit. ***Pick a number*** *and add your Communication bonus:*

- *If 2-6,* ***turn to 322.***
- *If 7-12,* ***turn to 404.***

392

You thank Mrs. Cox for her help. As she gets up to leave, she laughs and says: "Now if you need a bite while you're talking to all the others, you just send Silversmith around to me and I'll whip up something for you. You must keep your strength up when you're hunting for a murderer!" ***Turn to 505.***

393

You glance at the bedside table. It is placed so that a sleeper could reach it without standing up. The top is clear and its drawer is closed.

- *If you search the drawer,* ***turn to 480.***
- *Otherwise,* ***turn to 330.***

394

You decide there is nothing more to learn from the housemaid. You thank her and show her out. ***Turn to 126.***

395

Holmes listens to your evidence, then chuckles. "I think you are overly bold to name Watson and I when you have so little evidence. That is not sound detective work, sir."

- *If you investigate the case further,* ***turn to 490.***
- *If you would like Holmes to explain fully,* ***turn to 584.***
- *Otherwise,* ***turn to 203.***

9

396

"Milverton?" Gray mutters, "Did you know him, Fraser?"

"No, I cannot say that I do ... of course, I remember now!" the Lieutenant says suddenly. "It was all over the papers the day we got back from Scotland. He'd been murdered the night before."

"Murdered while you were in Scotland?" you ask.

"Yes," Gray answers, puzzled, "Though what would that matter to us, anyhow? We didn't know the man." You hurriedly reassure them that you have no thought to connect them to the death. ***Turn to 494.***

397

You suddenly remember how grateful Lord Ellington felt for your resolution of his problems. A letter of introduction from him would help you deal with any suspicion.

•*If you ask him for the letter,* ***turn to 291.***

•*If you go straight to the Countess,* ***turn to 572.***

398

Your inspection of the walls complete, you retrace your steps to the house. ***Turn to 325.***

399

"Whom did Mr. Milverton visit recently?" you ask.

The coachman pauses to think, then shakes his head. "I can't really say that I remember, sir. You go so many places with a man over the years, you can't really remember just who you went to when."

"Think hard, man," you urge. "Surely you can remember some of them."

Reynolds's face screws up in thought, but he shakes his head. "No sir, I cannot recall. I am sorry." ***Turn to 312.***

400

"Mr. Jenkins," you say, "you are familiar with Mr. Milverton's papers and with his business methods and affairs. You have admitted, without prejudice to yourself, that he kept papers which might be used for blackmail. Who might have wished him dead?" ***Pick a number*** *and add your Communication bonus:*

- *If 2-4,* ***turn to 192.***
- *If 5-12,* ***turn to 405.***

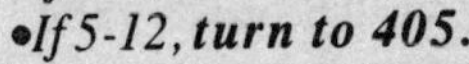

401

While the papers were thoroughly burnt, they were not broken up with a poker. Whoever burned them just threw them by the armload into the fire. It must have been burning very well indeed to destroy the papers, as the intruders did not have time to see that the work was done. *Check Clue F.* ***Turn to 529.***

402

The carpet reveals grim evidence of the crime. It is stained in spots with blood, and you can see that the man writhed in agony as he died. You consider the position of the marks, then nod. "It looks to me," you tell Lestrade, "as though Milverton was not standing here when he was first shot. He staggered from the area of the desk, fell, rolled over, and finally died. The pattern of the blood stains shows that he rolled on the floor. He must have been by the desk when he was knocked to the floor by the bullets, and as he staggered to his feet, was shot again. He then collapsed on the carpet."

"Possible," Lestrade agrees, "but of what use is it?" Spurred by his attitude, you return to your investigation. ***Turn to 623.***

403

The only part of the bedroom that you have not examined is the bath.

- *If you examine it,* ***turn to 549.***
- *Otherwise,* ***turn to 160.***

404

"Why did you let the papers burn?" you repeat.

"I didn't think we should touch anything until the police came," Jenkins repeats. "If we'd dashed over to the fire and pulled them out, we might have destroyed important traces of who killed Mr. Milverton."

You stare at Mr. Jenkins for some seconds after he gives this answer, then ask: "Was that your only reason?"

Jenkins blushes slightly, then frowns. "Well," he says, clearing his throat, "some of Mr. Milverton's business was of a very confidential nature, if you know what I mean, sir. Since he was dead it couldn't be carried on, for only he had the talent for it, and it seemed wise to let the papers burn. The law might have misinterpreted the letters." *Check Deduction 12.* ***Turn to 608.***

405

Jenkins sighs before speaking. "At times I suspected Mr. Milverton of blackmail, though I had no proof. Some of the letters he was unable to sell were connected to scandals — scandals which became public knowledge after the transaction failed."

Lestrade trades looks with you quickly, but fortunatley he doesn't interrupt Jenkins's elaborate self-justification.

With no help from you, Jenkins continues. "There were some people who might have felt they had grounds to kill the master. I did not see all his papers, and I am not certain he used every paper I saw, but some people might have felt that he wronged them. There were two brothers, John and James Patterson, whose funds were cut off by their family due to a scandal. Lady Eva Blackwell's forthcoming marriage to the Earl of Devoncourt was threatened, and the engagement of Colonel Dorking and Miss Miles broke up suddenly, only two days before the wedding. Finally, he had several flirtatious letters from Lady Blakeney. Her husband, the late Lord Harold, had been both an ambassador and Governor-General before his recent death. There may have been others, but those are the most recent matters that the master might have influenced." *Check Clue K.* ***Turn to 442.***

406

To summarize, a woman who rapidly fled Appledore Towers probably killed Milverton. According to the appointment book, Milverton had a midnight appointment with a woman, the Countess d'Albert's maid. You decide to wait a little before you pass this information on to Lestrade. *Check Deduction 10.* ***Turn to 390.***

407

You consider how your evidence fits together, and decide that two intruders must have hidden behind the curtains in the bay window while Milverton was in the room, and that they stayed hidden for quite a while.

- *If you checked Clues B, or Clues B & D,* ***turn to 220.***
- *If you checked Clue AA or Clue D,* ***turn to 550.***
- *Otherwise,* ***turn to 247.***

408

Watson gasps in astonishment at your question, then blurts out: "But that is almost as marvelous as Holmes' best work, cousin! Was it really that silly story that showed you it was us, or did you have other evidence and then use the story as a cover?"

Holmes tosses a disgusted look at Watson, then laughs. "You have seen me use that technique often enough, Watson," he says with a trace of bitterness. "You should not have let yourself be tricked by it. He had no evidence and knew nothing, but threw the question out on the chance that one of us would rise to the bait." Watson blushes and looks a little angry when he realizes his mistake. *Check Clue P.*

- *If you ask Holmes for more details,* ***turn to 224.***
- *Otherwise,* ***turn to 482.***

409

"We might learn something if we look at the body," you tell Lestrade. He agrees and you take a cab to the morgue, a grim gray building near Scotland Yard. The place has an atmosphere that makes you shudder—you wonder whether you would react this way if you didn't know what lay within its walls.

A constable waiting by the door quickly leads you to the surgery where Dr. Gordon has been examining the body. The doctor is a tall, grim-faced Scot, whose calm face and steady hands give an impression of competence and reliability. With hardly a word he removes the sheet from Milverton's body.

The victim was a short, stout bearded man with a plump face and receding hairline. You guess his age to be between forty and fifty. The small holes of his wounds mar the left side of his chest. There also is a slight scrape on his forehead.

When you straighten up from the corpse, the doctor gives his report. "Mr. Milverton was undoubtedly killed by six bullets in his chest," the doctor says grimly. "They were fired from very close range, as there were powder burns on his shirt. It was homicide, with so many shots at such a range." *Check Decision 8.*

- *If you ask what kind of gun was used,* ***turn to 155.***
- *Otherwise,* ***turn to 191.***

410

Now that you have completed your investigation at Appledore Towers, you try to develop some new lines of investigation for today.

- *If you checked Clue C and have not identified the two male intruders,* ***turn to 466.***
- *Otherwise,* ***turn to 290.***

411

It does not surprise you that Escott was Holmes. You knew already that Holmes and Watson were the intruders at Appledore Towers. Obviously, before burgling a house Holmes would have studied the house and grounds. You go to bed, eager to rise early again the next day. ***Turn to 278.***

412

"No, you and Watson did not kill Milverton," you say. "Neither of you is a murderer." ***Turn to 206.***

413

"Mr. Holmes," you say slowly, trying to choose your words with care. "If you were investigating this case, how would you go about identifying this mysterious woman? ***Pick a number*** *and add your Communication bonus:*

- *If 2-7,* ***turn to 337.***
- *If 8-12,* ***turn to 548.***

4

414

"I am surprised that the intruders came near the house, with so vicious a dog guarding it," you comment.

"The dog was locked up last night," the butler replies.

"If the dog had been out, Mr. Milverton might be alive today," you conclude.

"But the dog was locked up, just as Mr. Milverton had ordered," the butler replies, "so he hardly had a chance to influence matters. Do you have any other questions for me? We seem to be wasting time, time that you might better spend trying to find Mr. Milverton's killer."

- *If you ask Silversmith who could have locked up the dog,* ***turn to 321.***
- *Otherwise,* ***turn to 268.***

415

"Lady Eva," you say very gently, "I do not wish to upset or disturb you, but it is obvious that you are not telling me everything you know. You must have some more concrete reason to feel as you do." ***Pick a number*** *and add your Communication bonus:*

- *If 2-7,* ***turn to 272.***
- *If 8-12,* ***turn to 435.***

416

You remember Lord Ellington's gratitude when you solved his problem so quickly and quietly. Perhaps the peer will give you a letter of introduction, describing your competence and discretion.

- *If you ask Lord Ellington for a letter,* ***turn to 380.***
- *Otherwise,* ***turn to 386.***

417

"The night of the 13th?" Dorking repeats. "You do me more honour than I deserve to suggest that I might have helped slaughter the dog. As it happened, my nephew and I played whist until two in the morning, in the company of Mr. Carson and Lord Hardy. They took ten pounds apiece off of us, so they will remember the evening. I trust you will not bother them." ***Turn to 261.***

10

The boy gives a nod, as though he is settling his thoughts firmly into place. "I'm sure now, sir — I think the shots woke me up without my knowing what woke me, and I did see the woman. She must have been the killer. And when I woke again to all the yelling and running outside, I looked out the other window of my room and saw the men as they went over the wall — I wasn't sure because it was so mixed up with my dreams before — but from what Mr. Green said about how their looks, I think the men must have been Sherlock Holmes and his friend Dr. Watson."

"What?" you ask in astonishment. "We don't have time to waste with silly jokes, young man. What do you know of Sherlock Holmes and Dr. Watson?"

"I know Mr. Holmes is the greatest detective the world has ever seen," he answers quickly, "Mr. Milverton pointed them out to me one time, even before he visited Mr. Holmes at Baker Street."

"Why would Mr. Holmes and Dr. Watson visit Mr. Milverton at midnight?" Lestrade asks explosively. You manage to quiet him before he scares the boy into silence. "I figured that out too, sir," he answers brightly. "Mr. Milverton was probably working with them in some very mysterious matter, and they came to see him at a time when there would be no one else to disturb them. Then the woman came and murdered Mr. Milverton so quick that they didn't have time to stop her."

"Why would they flee the scene like criminals?" Lestrade demands, aghast at the boy's wild theory.

"The matter they were pursuing was very delicate, and they knew that their involvement would lead to revelations dangerous to the whole country," the boy answers eagerly. With another exchange of looks with Lestrade, you thank the boy for his help and watch him leave. *Check Clue N.*

•*If you ask Lestrade's about the boy's story,* ***turn to 223.***
•*Otherwise,* ***turn to 260.***

419

You wonder: what is the best approach in questioning the brothers?

- *If you say you're investigating blackmail,* ***turn to 208.***
- *If you say you're investigating Milverton's murder,* ***turn to 280.***

420

Both brothers look sharply at you, anger burning in their eyes. "And just what would this Mr. Milverton have to do with us?" James sneers.

- *If you checked Clue K,* ***turn to 427.***
- *Otherwise,* ***turn to 509.***

421

"You may leave, Mr. Jenkins," you say testily, "since you obviously would rather protect yourself against the remote chance of criminal charges, rather than help us apprehend Mr. Milverton's killer."

Jenkins leaves the room hurriedly. Lestrade consults his list and says that Mrs. Lindon, the housekeeper, is next.

- *If you talk to her,* ***turn to 246.***
- *Otherwise,* ***turn to 102.***

422

You try to order the course of events in your mind, then explain your confusion to Lestrade. "It makes less and less sense to me the more I examine the facts," you admit. "The intruders were in here for half an hour or more, opening the safe. Milverton sat at his desk for some time, reading and smoking his cigar as though he hadn't a care in the world, even though his safe had been broken open. Then the intruders decided to kill him."

"Milverton probably did not notice the safe," Lestrade replies. "The damage is not obvious unless you are near it. Perhaps the intruders hid and killed Milverton when he noticed them."

Puzzled, you try to figure out how the pieces fit together. ***Turn to 193.***

423

The bed is large and well-made, covered with fine sheets and warm blankets. The covers are folded back and the pillows fluffed, ready for their master to come in and lie down. The bed was not slept in the night before. "Well," you comment to Lestrade, "Milverton stayed up late last night."

"Strange," replies Silversmith. "That is highly unusual—the master habitually retired at ten-thirty every evening." *Check Deduction 4.* ***Turn to 393.***

424

"Do you have any idea who killed Mr. Milverton?" you ask.

"Well," he answers eagerly, "I'm just guessing because I didn't see much—but I think it might have been some spies or foreign agents." He goes on quickly when you stare at him in disbelief. "You see, Mr. Milverton called himself an agent, but everyone was always very careful not to talk about what he did. I think he did something very secret for England, and that foreign agents killed him to stop him." He hesitates, looking confused and thoughtful, then mutters: "Unless — Mr. Silversmith said it must have been a dream." ***Pick a number*** *and add your Observation bonus:*

- *If 2-5,* ***turn to 560.***
- *If 6-12,* ***turn to 511.***

425

You fit the clues together, then decide that after the intruders opened the safe, Milverton came in before they found what they wanted. The logical deduction seems to be that Milverton surprised them and was killed as a result.

- *If you checked Clue AA or Clue D,* ***turn to 135.***
- *Otherwise,* ***turn to 247.***

12

426

"You look like a discreet man," John Patterson says carefully. "We will trust you not to talk if our case does not affect your investigation." You nod, and he continues.

"We had every reason to know of Mr. Milverton," Patterson says bitterly. "My brother and I lived rather too well for a while, both in our nightlife and our visits to the turf. We paid Mr. Milverton to prevent his informing our uncle, who controls our money."

"You paid blackmail?" you ask.

"We were foolish enough to do that," James agrees. "Our uncle eventually learned of our indiscretions, through his own resources, and cut off our funds. That's why we moved to such restricted accommodations," James adds, indicating the small rooms with a sweep of his arm. ***Turn to 275.***

427

"Come now, gentlemen," you say gently. "I know from his papers that Mr. Milverton was very interested in your situation. As he was a notorious blackmailer, I would assume that he tried to do business with you."

The brothers exchange another glance. "We can't hide it, John," James says, and then turns to you. "Milverton blackmailed us, and we paid the villain. But unfortunately our uncle discovered our misdeeds anyway and cut us off." ***Turn to 275.***

428

"Could you tell anything special about the two men?" you ask, "other than the fact that one was tall and thin, the other short and stocky?"

"Oh, yes sir," he answers, "I got a good look at the one I grabbed. He was wearing a mask over his eyes, but he had a mustache and a strong jaw. When they was running, I could see that the tall man was a very good runner, very smooth. The other man ran well for his size, but he had just a hint of a limp. It didn't really slow him up, but there was something a little wrong with how he run."

•*If you ask him about the dog not barking,* ***turn to 555.***
•*Otherwise,* ***turn to 305.***

429

"What sort of master was Mr. Milverton?" you ask.

"He was a damned good master!" the coachman answers sharply. "He paid me half again as much as what most coachmen gets, and he never shouted at a man unless you deserved to be yelled at. And he was a kindly man—if he was going to be some little time, he'd tell you in advance and let you find somewhere warm to wait for him. I want to see the man what killed him swing for it, I tell you." ***Pick a number and add your Intuition bonus:***

- *If 2-7, **turn to 312.***
- *If 8-12, **turn to 376.***

2

430

In a flood of tears Mary Jones admits everything to you. "Oh, sir, it was my fiance's idea, and I did it so he could come visit me. We meant no harm by it, sir."

"Now just what did you do?" Lestrade asks.

"Oh, I locked up Brutus, so my fiance could come and walk out with me."

"On the night of the murder?" Lestrade asks eagerly.

"Yes, yes," she admits. "And what's worse, my fiance didn't even come to see me after I went to all that trouble, and I haven't heard from him at all since."

•*If you ask her to describe her fiance,* ***turn to 328.***
•*Otherwise,* ***turn to 394.***

431

The groom comes into the room. He's dressed in rough clothes, heavy grey pants, a red shirt and woolen vest, all worn and faded. "What did you see and hear during the murder?" you ask him.

"Oh, I'm hardly the one to ask, mate," he answers. "I just barely got in on the end of it. You see sir, I sleeps out in the stables, to be near the horses iffen there's any trouble with them at night. Well, I was sleeping, when I 'ears all this noise outside. When I run to the window I see all the other men running and yelling, and Reynolds yelled for me to come down and 'elp 'em, but by the time I got me trousers and boots on, it was all over. The blokes were gone over the wall and away."

•*If you ask him his opinion of Milverton,* ***turn to 580.***
•*Otherwise,* ***turn to 234.***

432

"When did this reconciliation with your uncle occur?" you ask pleasantly.

"It took weeks," James answers. "We had to prove we were willing to work hard. On the night of the 13th he invited us to dinner at his townhouse. The evening was so spirited that we stayed the night, and the next morning Uncle George restored our income." ***Turn to 449.***

10

433

"Silversmith," you continue, "I would appreciate it very much if you could tell me something about the other members of the staff before I question them. Anything that would help me question them more effectively."

"Why, I don't know sir," he replies in some confusion. "They are all very ordinary folk, I should say—nothing unusual about any of them."

"Oh come now," you say, "even if they are the most perfect staff in London, one or two of them must have peculiarities. Nothing wrong, just oddities."

The butler still seems hesitant. "Well, sir, if you put it that way, there are one or two things I might say. Mr. Jenkins, the master's secretary, is a very quiet and discreet man. He would never say anything about his work, not even to make himself look important. Mrs. Cox, the cook, was very popular with the master because she did her job so well, and he appreciated good food. She's also very fond of gossiping about the upper classes, and their doings, though she never does any harm by it. Mary Jones, the housemaid, is my niece. I keep half an eye on her in the evening, for she's got an eye for the young men, like all girls that age. And young Johnny, the page, thinks too much for his station. He's very excitable and has a vivid imagination — he sees wild possibilities in the simple situation." ***Turn to 448.***

434

"The true reason for my inquiries into blackmail," you say, "is to find the murderer of a man named Milverton, who was known to the police as a blackmailer..."

Before you can finish, James flares: "And if we answer your questions about this Milverton, I suppose next you shall want to know about some plot to fix the Grand National? Get out of here sir, for we have no use for snoops!" Concerned by their militant attitude, you hurriedly leave. ***Turn to 374.***

435

For a moment you're afraid Lady Eva will break down under your questioning. Almost visibly she pulls herself together, stifles a sob, and says slowly: "I have been assured that there is no chance of any of Mr. Milverton's papers ever hurting anyone again. My representative is in a position to know, and he has assured me that everything damaging to me was destroyed."

- *If you ask who represented her,* ***turn to 295.***
- *If you decide to leave,* ***turn to 333.***

436

You give the maid who has answered the door at Lady Eva's flat this note:

Lady Eva:

Your name has been mentioned to me in connection with a case of blackmail and murder, the murder of a man named Milverton. Both the police and I feel it best to deal with you privately, so that there is no undue mention of your name.

A few minutes later, a tall, angular woman of uncertain years comes out of Lady Eva's rooms. She introduces herself as Lady Eva's cousin, Phillippa, and says that you may come in and talk to Lady Eva. "But mind you," she adds, "if you hurt that poor girl, I shall see that you regret the day you were born." You follow her into a drawing room. ***Turn to 201.***

437

You must wait, despite your eagerness, until Lestrade picks you up in a cab and returns with you to Appledore Towers to interview the staff. It is a gorgeous day, though still crisp and cold. As the driver turns into the drive, a huge dog runs up, barking fiercely, and the man pulls back on the reins until one of the staff calms the beast.

Lestrade shakes his head a little. "Our burglars were fortunate," he mutters. "If they had encountered that brute, they never would have entered the study in the first place."

"Yes," you agree, thoughtfully. "It is odd that the dog didn't wake the house long before the gun was fired."

Lestrade leads you up to the house, greets Silversmith, and asks him for a room where you can interview the staff. The butler assures you that he is prepared for the request and has assembled the staff for you. ***Turn to 465.***

438

"What did you think of Mr. Milverton?" you ask.

The girl looks puzzled. "What is there to think of him, sir?" she answers. "He didn't bother me and he weren't never late paying us, so I guess he were as good a master as I could hope for. He were all right, long as you did your work, and with Mr. Silversmith and Mrs. Lindon, we couldn't ever not do all our work." ***Turn to 610.***

439

"So, once you had to give up the pursuit, you returned to the study to see if your master was dead or alive."

"Yes," Silversmith confirms. "Mr. Jenkins, the secretary went with me. The key was in the outside door and we opened it and went in. We could then see at a glance that Mr. Milverton was dead. We looked around but didn't touch anything. His desk was disturbed, as though he'd fallen across it, and the curtains across the bay window were partly open, which was not usual after dark. The fire was burning brightly, with papers in it, and the safe was open." ***Pick a number** and add your Intuition bonus:*

- *If 2-7,* ***turn to 178.***
- *If 8-12,* ***turn to 587.***

440

"I hardly see how our movements are of concern in the case," John Patterson snaps. "You need waste no more time here, sir." ***Turn to 509.***

441

"Do you have any idea who might have killed Mr. Milverton?" you ask.

The question panics the girl, as you should have expected. "What's that, sir?" she asks. "Who killed Mr. Milverton? How should I know? I don't have no idea! Please sir, you don't think I know anything do you?" She turns toward Lestrade, begging: "Tell him you know I wouldn't have anything to do with killing the master! Please sir, before he has me taken away sir!" You and Lestrade manage to ease her hysterics but it is obvious that you won't get anything useful out of her. As Mrs. Lindon leads the sobbing girl away you get an earfull of the housekeeper's harsh opionions. ***Turn to 624.***

442

You thank Jenkins for his help, and the secretary scurries out of the room. Lestrade consults his list and tells you that Mrs. Lindon, the housekeeper, is the next witness.

- *If you talk to her,* ***turn to 246.***
- *Otherwise,* ***turn to 102.***

443

You look squarely at the housemaid. "Did you lock up the dog so your boyfriend could come to see you?" you ask. "Come, girl, there's no need to protect him—after all he's abandoned you hasn't he?"

"I did lock up Brutus," she admits. "My boyfriend suggested it so he could come to see me. And he was so kind, I couldn't resist." She starts to cry a little. "You don't think that helped those men kill Mr. Milverton do you. It's not my fault, is it?"

"Oh no," you assure her, "it's not your fault. Don't worry about it any more."

•*If you ask her to describe her fiance,* ***turn to 328.***
•*Otherwise,* ***turn to 394.***

444

As the four-wheeler grinds its way through the streets of London, you consider Inspector Lestrade's claim that Holmes was too busy to take the case. "Mr. Holmes was too busy to investigate the murder, Mr. Lestrade?" you ask, suspicion strong in your voice. "That doesn't ring true somehow, sir. I'd have heard something of it from my cousin, Dr. Watson, if Mr. Holmes were so busy."

Lestrade looks a little embarassed. "Well, sir, I may not have stated matters with the exactness you have the right to expect from me. Mr. Holmes did not take the case because the murdered man was a blackmailing villain, and Mr. Holmes therefore assumed that the murderer had due cause. As a representative of the law, I cannot accept this assumption, and since Mr. Holmes cannot possibly know the identity of the killer, he cannot be certain that the killer had any justification at all." You nod a little to encourage his discussion. "But there it is, sir: will you still take the case?" *Check Deduction 6.*

"Very well, Mr. Lestrade," you say slowly, "I will undertake the case, with this understanding — I must consult with Mr. Holmes before I tell you whom I think is guilty."

The police detective considers this, then nods. "I suppose I must agree to that, as I tried to deceive you. Now let me tell you what we know so far." ***Turn to 144.***

6

445

"I appreciate your viewpoint, Mr. Holmes," you say, "and I respect it. It does not seem proper to quit my investigation until I identify the killer and the motive."

Holmes holds up his hand. "Very well," he tells you, "search for your murderer. But I demand one pledge from you. If you do discover the killer, first tell me." Holmes' sincerety forces you to agree. You return to your lodgings and go to bed, in order to rise early on the morrow. *Check Deduction 10.* ***Turn to 278.***

446

"I learned one thing I find difficult to understand," you begin, looking at Holmes, "especially difficult because you disliked the man so thoroughly."

"You wish to know why Milverton came to see me last week," Holmes replies. "You know that my business requires discretion, but I will tell you this. Our discussion involved the affairs of one of my clients, and the identity of that client or the subject of our discussion will not help you in locating the killer." It is obvious that Holmes will say nothing more on this aspect of the matter. ***Turn to 293.***

447

You decide that the material on top of the desk is not useful to your investigation.

•*If you search inside the desk,* ***turn to 596.***
•*Otherwise,* ***turn to 216.***

448

You wonder if the butler could tell you anything useful about Milverton's big watchdog.

•*If you ask about the dog,* ***turn to 627.***
•*Otherwise,* ***turn to 268.***

449

After a little casual talk, you thank the Patterson for their help and leave their flat. ***Turn to 374.***

450

You see that the intruders cut the glass out of the door, then reached through the hole to open the lock from the inside. The intruder made the cut very cleanly and smoothly, and picked just the right spot on the door.

"Look closely at this, Mr. Lestrade," you say, feeling a little excitement. "Do you agree that that is a very neat, almost professional piece of work on this door. Someone knew exactly what he was doing to open it like that."

"So he did, so he did," the Inspector agrees. "An unusual talent for a gentleman, if I am correct in my opinion that he was a blackmail victim trying to destroy evidence or seek revenge."

You think for a moment, then ask: "Could the intruders have been burglars hired by a victim or victims of Mr. Milverton to obtain the compromising papers he held?"

Lestrade shakes his head. "I considered that possibility, but it would not make sense. If you had already been blackmailed, you would hardly put yourself in the hands of another criminal by hiring him to do such a job. The murder works against that theory also. A professional burglar might have knocked out Milverton , but burglars seldom carry guns. The noise hardly suits quiet theft, and most of them have a wholesome fear of the rope." ***Turn to 222.***

451

"I am looking into some matters mentioned in the popular press," you explain. "I regret to have read that you and your husband have recently separated. It might help me if you could tell me what caused this unfortunate event."

The old woman's eyes flash, and she answers fiercely: "It would be useful if you learned how to behave like a gentleman. That is no business of anyone but my husband's and my own, and nothing to do with a murder! Jeffreys," she says to the butler, "Show this fellow out at once!" With another bow, you follow the butler out. A wasted visit! ***Turn to 463.***

452

From marks by the wall, you see that one of the men fell on his way down. You wonder whether he hurt himself in the accident. When you attempt to follow the footprints across the heath, you quickly lose the trail and cannot find it again. You learn nothing more here. ***Turn to 387.***

453

"I believe that Lady Blakeney killed Milverton," you say. "She blamed Milverton for her husband's death."

"What evidence do you have for the charge?" Holmes demands, as Watson leans forward eagerly to listen to you.

•*If you checked Clue Y,* ***turn to 604.***

•*Otherwise,* ***turn to 606.***

454

Jenkins, Milverton's secretary, mentioned people whom his master might have blackmailed. Obviously, these individuals form the most logical group to visit in the hunt for his murderer. *Check Decision 17.* ***Turn to 230.***

455

You walk along the wall a few yards to get well clear of the intruders' tracks, then brush away the glass and pull yourself over the wall. Grunting with exertion, Lestrade follows. "I will await you at the house, if I may be of further help," Silversmith calls from across the wall.

You return to the spot where the intruders crossed and search the ground for any sign of their crossing the heath.

•*If you have checked Decisions 1 and 2,* ***turn to 471.***
•*If you have checked either Decision 1 or 2,* ***turn to 182.***
•*If you have checked neither Decision,* ***turn to 489.***

456

You continue to run through the evidence in your mind, trying to identify the most useful information.

•*If you checked Clue M,* ***turn to 528.***
•*Otherwise,* ***turn to 351.***

457

"Tell us about the staff," you finally ask. "What sort of people do you have working here?"

Silversmith's face looks as if it were carved from marble. "I have no idea what sort of information you want, sir," he says coldly. "If there were anything discreditable about any of Mr. Milverton's staff, we would have discharged them long ago." You wonder if you can get any more useful information from the angry butler.

•*If you ask him about the dog,* ***turn to 414.***
•*If you are done with Silversmith,* ***turn to 268.***

458

The butler stiffens slightly, stares at you, then looks at his watch in apparent alarm. "Why, look at the time!" he says. "I am sorry but I must be about my duties. Good day." ***Turn to 294.***

459

You approach Lady Eva's flat, knock and ask for her. Instead of Lady Eva, the maid takes you to her cousin, Miss Phillippa Blackwell, a tall, angular, hard-featured woman of uncertain age. She enters reading the credentials you sent in when you asked for Lady Eva.

"What do you want?" she demands harshly. "What possible business could an investigator have with a young woman preparing for her marriage? If you make any trouble for my cousin, I shall make you wish that you had never been born." Hurriedly you try to explain why you have come there. ***Pick a number*** *and add your Communication bonus: (Add 2 if you checked Decision 20.)*

•*If 2-8,* ***turn to 379.***
•*If 9-12,* ***turn to 111.***

460

You have assembled all the evidence that you will be able to find in this investigation. Wondering if you can name the killer, correctly, you go to Baker Street to check your conclusions with Sherlock Holmes. Mrs. Hudson takes you up to the

rooms Holmes shares with Watson.

"Your cousin is back, Watson," Holmes says cheerfully. "Perhaps he will tell us who killed Milverton." You nod.

•*If you checked Clue P,* ***turn to 203.***
•*Otherwise,* ***turn to 303.***

461

You take each book from the shelf and flip through it. Most of the books seem to deal with business, estate management, or law, though there are some literary classics mixed among them. You notice that Milverton had a fine collection of guides to the old families and great names in society, very valuable tomes for a man in Milverton's nefarious business. There is nothing hidden in any of the books. ***Turn to 478.***

462

"Escott," the peddler says, "No sir, I can't say I ever heard of the bloke. You the law or something, to be hunting a man and not know where he lives or works?" He turns and hurries over to a group of people, offering his flowers and pointedly cutting off his conversation with you. ***Turn to 516.***

463

The next name on your list of possible blackmail victims is Captain Grey, who recently had an appointment as an attache cancelled.

•*If you go to see him,* ***turn to 497.***
•*Otherwise,* ***turn to 230.***

464

"Mr. Jenkins," you say sternly, "you're obviously trying to find a reasonable explanation for an action you cannot defend, but you know it won't do you any good. Why did you let the papers burn?" ***Pick a number*** *and add your Communication bonus:*

•*If 2-6,* ***turn to 583.***
•*If 7-12,* ***turn to 573.***

465

Silversmith leads you to a small parlour and shows you to a chair by a small table. The table has pens, ink and paper for you to take notes, as well as chairs for Lestrade and the witnesses. "Whom do you wish to see first, Inspector?" the butler inquires.

Lestrade consults a list. "Green, the undergardener," he says. "This is the man who almost caught one of the intruders," Lestrade explains to you.

The undergardener is a typical servent, a solidly built, stolid man in his early twenties. When asked, he tells his story simply.

"Well, sir," he begins, "I was sleeping, when suddenly I hears three or four loud bangs. Then Silversmith starts yelling for everyone to come quickly, that the master might be in trouble. Well I pulls on my trousers, sticks my feet in my boots without stopping to lace them, and runs for Mr. Milverton's study. That door was locked, so we went dashing through the front door and around the corner of the house. We saw two men vanishing off the far end of the veranda, and went running in that direction, though they was ducking through the garden so clever that it was almost impossible to follow them."

"Then what happened?" you ask.

"I got a look at them as they came out of the trees near the wall. One was tall and thin, the other short and stocky, and I knowed neither was one of us. I yelled for the others as I run up. The tall bloke just about jumped over the wall, he was so spry, but the other had to pull himself up and over. I grabbed his ankle, but he kicked me in the chops and was over and gone before I got back up." ***Pick a number*** *and add your Intuition bonus:*

- *If 2-6,* ***turn to 481.***
- *If 7-12,* ***turn to 428.***

466

You remember that the tracks of the two intruders went all the way across the heath. They probably hailed a cab and returned to their own home. You wonder how to find the cabbie. ***Pick a number*** *and add your Scholarship bonus:*

- *If 2-5,* ***turn to 519.***
- *If 6-12,* ***turn to 586.***

467

You pause to consider the evidence. Two men came in, taking some time to open the safe, then hid for some time behind the curtains. It seems possible that when they found that Milverton was not asleep, they waited for him to return to his room with the intent to kill him.

- *If you checked Clue AA or Clue D,* ***turn to 135.***
- *Otherwise,* ***turn to 247.***

468

Indignantly you chase the drunken driver from your rooms. He offers no violence, though muttering many an oath at your rudeness and cruelty. *Check Clue V.* ***Turn to 351.***

469

"I believe I saw Lady Blakeney once," you say thoughtfully. "At least I assumed it was she, for it was one of the most beautiful women I have ever seen."

The butler almost smiles. "That would be her, sir. A tall, dark woman, with the strong sort of beauty. She has a thin mouth, curved nose, and dark eyebrows that heighten the fire in her eyes." You nod in agreement. *Check Deduction 19.* ***Turn to 483.***

470

"From what you saw and know yourself, what happened here on the night of the murder?" you ask the butler.

"For the most part it was a like any other evening, sir. As usual I made sure all the outside doors were properly locked at ten, except the one into Mr. Milverton's private study. He always locked that one himself. The master was playing billiards and having a cigar; after I locked up I asked him if he needed anything. He told me no, and that I might go on to bed, which I proceeded to do.

"I was sleeping soundly when suddenly I heard a series of sharp cracks, a pause, then another. I recognized them as gunshots, and realized they came from the master's study. As I grabbed my robe and put on my slippers, I called for the staff to come and help. We went down the passage to the study, and found the door locked. Then we ran around and saw two men running away. I looked in the study window and saw the master lying on the floor, so I shouted for the others to catch the intruders. But they were too quick, and got over the wall and away across the heath. Green got a hand on one, but the man kicked free."

- *If you ask why the staff stopped at the wall,* ***turn to 200.***
- *Otherwise,* ***turn to 439.***

471

You regret the time you spent following other leads now, for the sun has burned away much of the frost, almost obliterating the tracks of the two men from the grass. ***Pick a number*** *and add your Observation bonus:*

- *If 2-7,* ***turn to 491.***
- *If 8-10,* ***turn to 452.***
- *If 11-12,* ***turn to 276.***

472

Looking more closely at the woman's tracks, you discover a few of the small pebbles that formed the ornamental border of the drive. This confirms your deduction that the woman must have been a stranger. *Check Clue B.*

- *If you checked Decision 1,* ***turn to 602.***
- *Otherwise,* ***turn to 149.***

473

The page's confused look turns to one of fear at your question, and he answers hurriedly, "Oh, no sir, I couldn't even begin to make a guess. The woman must have been a dream too. I shouldn't even talk about such things. I really don't know anything more. May I go now?" The boy is so scared it's useless to ask him more questions. ***Turn to 560.***

474

Lestrade actually smiles, and he doesn't even have to look over his list this time. "We've finally got to the end of them," he says, still smiling. "The only one left is the page, Johnny. Do you want to talk to him?"

- *If you talk to the page,* ***turn to 520.***
- *Otherwise,* ***turn to 235.***

475

"Now you should know that you have nothing to worry about Miss Jones," you say gently. "Why are you so nervous?" ***Pick a number*** *and add your Communication bonus:*

- *If 2-8,* ***turn to 503.***
- *If 9-12,* ***turn to 430.***

476

You have completed your examination of Milverton's study and consider further steps. Lestrade asks you if you want to search the bedroom as well.

•*If you search the bedroom,* ***turn to 377.***
•*Otherwise,* ***turn to 160.***

477

"Aside from the other reasons why these gentlemen did not burgle Appledore Towers that night," Holmes continues, "I do not see how you can believe that they possessed the skill to sneak in and to open the safe. I understand that the job was done in the most professional manner."

•*If you want to investigate the case further,* ***turn to 490.***
•*If you want an explanation from Holmes,* ***turn to 568.***

478

You return to where you started, look at the door to the passage that leads to the parlour, and hunt for any marks left by the intruders. ***Pick a number*** *and add your Observation bonus:*

•*If 2-6,* ***turn to 238.***
•*If 7-12,* ***turn to 373.***

479

You search for the proper phrasing. "Colonel Dorking," you begin, "I must ask this for the formality of it. Where were you at midnight on the 13th?" ***Pick a number*** *and add your Communication bonus: (Add 3 if you checked Decision 20.)*

•*If 2-7,* ***turn to 302.***
•*If 8-12,* ***turn to 417.***

480

You pull open the drawer of the small table and find a handkerchief, a small bottle of cough medicine, and a revolver. A quick examination reveals that the gun is loaded. "Mr. Milverton seems to have entertained some doubts about his safety," you comment.

Lestrade nods slowly. "Yes, he did, little good that it did him. His fears were well-justified." ***Turn to 330.***

481

You ponder Green's remarks and try to fit them with what you have learned already.

•*If you ask him about the dog not barking,* ***turn to 555.***
•*Otherwise,* ***turn to 305.***

482

To Watson's relief, you decide not to ask any more questions. After a little more small talk you bid them a good evening and leave Baker Street. The next day you rise early and breakfast quickly, ready to pursue evidence in new directions. ***Turn to 410.***

483

You continue to chat with the butler. ***Pick a number*** *and add your Communication bonus: (Add 2 if you checked Decision 20.)*

•*If 2-7,* ***turn to 531.***
•*If 8-12,* ***turn to 180.***

484

You write a few notes, trying to organize your ideas.

•*If you checked Decision 17,* ***turn to 169.***
•*Otherwise,* ***turn to 493.***

485

You ponder the evidence for a moment, wondering how to uncover evidence that will identify the two intruders.

•*If you checked Clue N,* ***turn to 579.***
•*Otherwise,* ***turn to 187.***

486

The drive consists of grey gravel, packed and rolled firmly to make a surprisingly smooth surface. Neither the driveway nor the grass beside it show any distinct footprints. ***Turn to 138.***

487

You are unable to find anything else of interest in the notebook. Glancing at Lestrade, you drop it back in the desk drawer. ***Turn to 216.***

488

Should you visit the Hornet or Mr. Osborne?

• *If you visit the newspaper,* ***turn to 383.***
• *If you visit Osborne,* ***turn to 250.***

489

You study the tracks left by the intruders. The sun is just starting to burn off the frost, and you are pleased that you didn't delay any longer in beginning to examine this portion of the trail. ***Pick a number*** *and add your Observation bonus:*

• *If 2-3,* ***turn to 491.***
• *If 4-6,* ***turn to 452.***
• *If 7-12,* ***turn to 276.***

490

Your investigation has not been a complete success. You may wish to investigate this case again, to see if you can solve it completely.

• *If you start over from the beginning,* ***turn to the Prologue.***
• *If you begin with the interviews of Milverton's staff,* ***turn to 465.***

491

The tracks on the heath have faded away too much for you to follow the trail. ***Turn to 387.***

492

You see that the intruders cut the glass out of the door and then reached inside to open the lock. The job was likely done neatly and quietly. ***Turn to 222.***

493

The last name on your list is Lady Sylvia Daniels. Should you try to visit her?

•*If you see her,* ***turn to 578.***
•*Otherwise,* ***turn to 169.***

494

You thank Captain Gray and Lieutenant Fraser for their help and leave the barracks. ***Turn to 230.***

495

You quietly return to the neighborhood of Miss Miles, and study her house. Unfortunately, her neighbors are having a party, and there are several private guards around the area. It would be mad to attempt burglary with those about. You return home, happy they did not notice you. ***Turn to 460.***

496

You cannot think of a good source of gossip, until it occurs to you that Inspector Lestrade may be able to tell you something. ***Turn to 185.***

497

The underground takes you to the barracks of Grey's regiment, and an orderly shows you in to see the Captain. *Deduct 2 pence from your Character Record.* Another officer, Lieutenant Fraser, is with him. You notice that Grey is tall and slender, while Fraser is short and stocky, with a bulldog jaw and neatly- trimmed mustache. They carefully read your credentials, then ask why you came to see them.

"As Inspector Lestrade's letter says," you answer, "I am helping the police on a delicate matter. It has been suggested to me that you might be able to shed some light on some related affairs."

"A delicate matter?" Fraser asks. When you nod he turns to Grey and says: "Perhaps I should leave, Henry, and allow you privacy."

The captain shakes his head. "No John, please stay. From my recent experience I've discovered that too much privacy is not desirable, even in personal matters." He turns to you and says: "How can we assist you?"

- *If you ask him why his appointment as attache was cancelled,* ***turn to 569.***
- *If you explain that you may have to deal with General Edwards, who cancelled the appointment,* ***turn to 523.***

498

"I understand that you feed the dog, Helen," you say.

"Yes, I do," she admits cautiously.

"The dog was locked up last night. Were you the one who took care of that?"

"No one said I did, did they?" She seems near the edge of panic. "Oh, I wouldn't dare try to tie up Brutus. He's much too big for me to do that. I'm just glad he takes his food from me without having me for dessert!" ***Turn to 384.***

499

"No, Mr. Holmes," you say. "Neither you nor Dr. Watson killed Milverton. I have evidence that he received a lady visitor that night, and I am certain that she must have been the killer."

"Who was the lady?" Holmes asks.

- *If you admit you have no idea,* ***turn to 525.***
- *Otherwise,* ***turn to 524.***

3

500

You quietly travel to the neighborhood of Lady Sylvia's mansion. All of the houses around here have extensive grounds, and there are many trees along the streets. You should be able to scale the fence without anyone noticing you.

As at Appledore Towers, there is broken glass scattered across the top of the fence. Using the sleeve of your jacket you knock the glass away, then grip the wall and pull yourself to the top. As you swing one leg over, and get ready to drop to the ground inside, you hear loud barking. A dog bigger than Milverton's Brutus bounds towards you, and you pull your leg back and drop to the street just before the beast hurls itself at the wall. You return to your rooms, relieved that you saw him while you still had a chance to escape. ***Turn to 460.***

501

"Milverton!" the Colonel shouts, then sighs. "I have no real wish to help you catch his killer, sir. I should have killed him myself!"

"What did he do?" you ask.

"Why, the devil found evidence of some indiscreet behavior of mine — typical young man's folly, you understand. He said he would prevent my wedding if I didn't pay him five thousand pounds. Being a fool, I paid. What I didn't know was that he had also blackmailed Miss Miles, my fiance, and she refused to pay. He revealed her secrets in ways that made the wedding impossible, curse him. But someone paid him in the manner he deserved."

- *If you ask where he was during the murder,* ***turn to 479.***
- *If you thank him and leave,* ***turn to 261.***

502

You can think of nothing more that would be useful to ask Lady Eva. ***Turn to 370.***

503

Mary Jones looks very upset at the thought that she could be nervous. "Nervous," she finally says, "I'm not nervous at all. Whatever makes you think that I am? It's not that I'm nervous at all. No honest person likes to sit for hours being questioned about something so dreadful as this killing. Can't you leave a poor working girl alone?" ***Turn to 394.***

504

You approach the bookcase and examine it carefully. It is a solidly-made piece of furniture, filled with a variety of books. A bust of Athena sits atop the case. You look around carefully and satisfy yourself that nothing is hidden behind it.

•*If you search the books one by one,* ***turn to 461.***
•*Otherwise,* ***turn to 478.***

505

Once more Lestrade consults his list. "The kitchen maid is next," he says, "if you have any questions for her."

•*If you want to talk to her,* ***turn to 232.***
•*Otherwise,* ***turn to 624.***

506

As soon as you re-enter the grounds, you circle the walls of the estate, looking over the glass on top. None of it has been disturbed; you realize that the wall was only crossed at the spot where the intruders fled. The men must have entered by the front gate. ***Turn to 325.***

507

You realize you must stay at your lodgings until ten to see if a driver responds to your ad. The time crawls by, and you find that you cannot concentrate on your morning newspaper.

•*If you checked Clue R or Clue U,* ***turn to 287.***
•*Otherwise,* ***turn to 163.***

508

"The men were Captain Grey and Lieutenant Fraser," you tell Holmes. "They sought vengeance for the harm Milverton's blackmail did to Grey's career."

"No, no," Holmes says, "it could hardly have been them. There was a mention in the newspapers that they returned to London by train the morning after the murder. And aside from that, I have learned from my sources that Milverton had nothing to do with Grey's problems." ***Turn to 477.***

509

Both Pattersons stare militantly at you, as though daring you. You realize that you have no evidence to force them to answer your questions. With a brief word and stiff nod you leave their flat. ***Turn to 374.***

510

"Who killed Milverton?" you ask. "You and Watson witnessed the killing, did you not?"

Holmes nods. "I will tell you on one condition," he says. "You must not reveal the solution to anyone. Lestrade must not cause any trouble in the matter."

"I shall do as you wish, Mr. Holmes."

"Lady Blakeney killed Milverton," Holmes says. "I do not use the term murder. Milverton blackmailed her, and because she would not or could not pay what he demanded, he sent letters to her husband that implied infidelity on her part. Her husband died from grief, as he was already quite sick at the time. Since she could not prosecute Milverton without ruining herself, Watson and I agree that the killing was substantially justified."

"Was there much evidence pointing to her?" you ask.

"All too much, I fear," Holmes answers. "Lestrade might solve this, in spite of himself. Of all the suspects victims, she had the strongest motive, avenging the recent death of her husband. She had to communicate with Milverton to set up the fatal appointment, and there is a strong chance that someone saw her as she went to, or from, Appledore Towers. It also could probably be shown that she owns, or has owned, a gun like the one that killed Milverton." You talk a little longer with Holmes and Watson, trying to learn how to solve such a case more successfully in the future. **THE END.**

511

The change in Johnny's voice catches your attention. What was this dream that Silversmith had apparently told him not to discuss?

•*If you ask him about it,* ***turn to 595.***
•*Otherwise,* ***turn to 560.***

512

After dinner at your lodgings, you try to think of anything useful you might do during the evening. Or would a good night's rest improve your chance of finding a solution?

•*If you checked Deduction 6,* ***turn to 288.***
•*Otherwise,* ***turn to 556.***

513

You consider Holmes' words, then agree. "Very well Mr. Holmes, I shall drop the case," you say slowly. "I trust your judgement, although I do not know how you can be so certain that the killing was justified."

Holmes smiles thinly, then makes you swear never to repeat what you hear. Once you agree he says, "Tell him, Watson."

•*If you wish to hear the explanation,* ***turn to 179.***
•*Otherwise,* ***turn to the Prologue.***

514

You find several stray men, vendors and laborers on their way home. You offer them four shillings to pretend to fight each other, to create a noise that will allow you to play a joke on some friends. They take the money and go down the street a little way as you instructed, vanishing into the fog. *Deduct the money from your Character Record.* ***Pick a number*** *and add your Communication bonus:*

•*If 2-6,* ***turn to 183.***
•*If 7-12,* ***turn to 116.***

515

You stretch your legs out and dodge a different direction at every corner. With the help of the fog, you leave the bobbie far behind you. ***Turn to 460.***

516

A little desperate, you try to figure out how to locate this mysterious plumber. ***Pick a number*** *and add your Scholarship bonus:*

•*If 2-7,* ***turn to 142.***
•*If 8-12,* ***turn to 161.***

517

You try to pick up speed, but the bobbie is a good runner and closes in on you. Trying to evade him, you duck up a small alley, only to find that it runs into a wall too high for you to climb. As you turn around you, find the bobbie blocking your escape.

•*If you surrender,* ***turn to 553.***
•*If you attack him,* ***turn to 518.***

518

As he calls on you to surrender, you charge the bobbie, trying to drive a shoulder into his stomach before he can lay you out with his club. ***Pick a number*** *and add your Athletics bonus:*

- *If 2-9,* ***turn to 521.***
- *If 10-12,* ***turn to 526.***

519

You cannot think of an efficient way to trace down the cabbie who picked up the intruders. You remember that Holmes sometimes uses his Baker Street Irregulars in similar searches, but you do not know any of them. ***Turn to 290.***

520

Johnny the page is still a boy, perhaps 15 or 16, with bright eyes and a sharp, intelligent face. He reminds you of a Baker Street Irregular employed by Sherlock Holmes. You ask him what he saw when Milverton was murdered.

He looks a little puzzled, then shakes his head. "I can't say I saw much of anything," he says. "I sleep up in the attic rather than in back with the rest, so I couldn't get down in time to join in the chase."

•*If you ask him his opinion of Mr. Milverton,* ***turn to 162.***
•*Otherwise,* ***turn to 560.***

521

As you charge the bobbie, his stick rises and falls, knocking you unconscious.

You awake in a cell in Cannon Row, with Inspector Lestrade glaring down at you.

"Bloody amateurs," the detective mutters. "I should have my head examined before I engage the help of a fool like you. Burglary! And assaulting one of my men as well! What were you thinking of?"

"There was evidence I had to get," you mutter.

"There is no evidence that justifies that sort of behavior. I will see Mr. Holmes and force an explanation from him. As for you, I think the magistrate will give you about thirty days to regret your actions. And if you say one word about me in court, you shall serve thirty months." The angry Inspector stomps out of your cell.

Gripping your aching head in both hands, you bury your head in the miserable pillow of your bunk. What a disastrous end to your investigation! For you, this case is over. **THE END.**

522

The drive consists of grey gravel, packed and rolled firmly to make a surprisingly smooth surface. Neither the driveway nor the grass beside it shows any clear footprints. Then you take another look at the drive. While most of its width is gravel, on each edge there is a six-inch border of tiny colored pebbles carefully placed to produce bands of different colors. At two or three places they show signs of having been disturbed by someone's foot, but there are no distinct tracks.

"This pattern of colored pebbles is rather odd," you comment to Lestrade and the butler. "Rather an attractive touch, I must admit."

"Yes, sir," Silversmith answers, "yes, indeed. That was one of Mr. Milverton's fancies, sir. He was very particular about it too, and insisted that the staff take great care not to walk on the borders." *Check Clue A.* ***Turn to 138.***

523

"Thank you, Captain," you begin. "I am afraid I may touch on an unpleasant matter for you, but I must consult General Edwards in this case, and I would appreciate your advice on how to deal with him."

"Why, you should have no trouble," Grey answers bitterly. "General Edwards will talk to anyone as long as there is no trace of scandal attached to their name to sully the purity of his own fame. But he heard that I was found alone with a young woman in a state of undress, and he immediately decided he wanted nothing to do with me."

•*If you ask him what caused the scandal,* ***turn to 274.***
•*If you ask if he heard of Milverton,* ***turn to 153.***

524

Drawing a deep breath, you prepare to tell Holmes which woman killed Milverton.

•*If you name Miss Miles,* ***turn to 114.***
•*If you name Lady Eva Blackwell,* ***turn to 562.***
•*If you name Lady Blakeney,* ***turn to 453.***
•*If you name Miss Phillippa Blackwell,* ***turn to 603.***

525

"I do not know who murdered Milverton," you admit.

•*If you try to solve the case again,* ***turn to 490.***
•*If you ask Holmes to exaplain,* ***turn to 510.***

526

You duck under the swinging club and double up the bobbie with a hard punch to his stomach. As he gasps for breath, you dash up the street, running like a madman. The thickening fog hides you from further pursuit and you get away. ***Turn to 460.***

527

"When we came here, we heard that huge dog of Mr. Milverton's barking, and got a look at him," you begin. "He's quite a dog, but I understood you can lock him up when it is necessary."

"Yessir," Yates answers. "Me and Brutus are proper mates, and never have a harsh word between us. Oh, if he'd been loose there wouldn't 'ave been no intruders in Mr. Milverton's study to shoot him up. No sir, there wouldn't 'ave been any bloke who would dare such a thing."

•*If you ask him if he locked up the dog,* ***turn to 210.***
•*Otherwise,* ***turn to 619.***

528

In thinking through the evidence you remember Escott, the plumber who asked Mary Jones to tie up the watchdog, and then did not visit her. Could he have been used by the intruders to clear one obstacle from their path?

•*If you decide to locate Escott,* ***turn to 177.***
•*Otherwise,* ***turn to 351.***

529

You have gone over the entire study except for the bay window near the fireplace. The curtains are partially open.

•*If you examine the bay window,* ***turn to 165.***
•*Otherwise,* ***turn to 476.***

530

"No sir, I can't say I knew him," the cabbie answers. "But there weren't no one else about sir, it must have been your friends." He thanks you and leaves when you give him his reward. *Deduct 5 shillings from your Character Record. Check Clue U.* ***Turn to 351.***

531

You continue to talk to the butler, trying to think of what questions might draw useful information from him. ***Pick a number*** *and add your Intuition bonus:*

- *If 2-7,* ***turn to 294.***
- *If 8-12,* ***turn to 538.***

532

"I believe Colonel Dorking and his nephew were the men," you say. "They had a motive — Milverton blackmailed the Colonel and ruined his marriage."

Holmes shakes his head. "You should read the papers more closely—there was a note in a social column that they spent that evening at the Colonel's club." ***Turn to 477.***

533

Once in the lane behind the house you hurry away through the fog. No one tries to stop you. ***Turn to 460.***

534

Hoping that Milverton might have left something useful in his clothes, you go through all of them carefully, searching all the pockets and feeling the linings for any hidden pockets. You even take the trouble to feel inside the shoes. However, your search uncovers nothing, and you close the wardrobe, convinced that it holds no useful evidence. ***Turn to 403.***

535

It is almost ten o'clock when there is a sharp knock at your door. You open it and a man enters. He is heavy, of average height, and has a hard face and red nose. "Morning sir," he says. "Are you the man who placed the ad in the paper this morning, about some passengers?"

"Yes, I am," you say. "Did you carry them?"

"I think I might have, sir," he answers, "I think I did. T'was on after midnight, sir, and mortal cold. Two men comes up to me and says they needs to go to Oxford Street. In they hopped and I took them."

"Can you describe them?' you ask.

"After a fashion sir, I guess I can. One man was tall and lean, the other was more my height, a stoutly built chap. They were both dressed in evening clothes under their greatcoats, though it was an odd place to pick such men up. And they was breathing hard, too, like they'd been running."

"Thank you," you answer, "those are my friends, I think. Did you recognize either of them?" *Check Clue W.* ***Pick a number*** *and add your Communication bonus:*

- *If 2-8,* ***turn to 530.***
- *If 9-12,* ***turn to 365.***

536

As you drop into the lane behind the house, a police constable swings around the corner and sees you. At his shout to stop, you run in the opposite direction at your best speed. ***Pick a number*** *and add your Athletics bonus:*

- *If 2-6,* ***turn to 517.***
- *If 7-12,* ***turn to 515.***

537

Lestrade looks over at you, his eyes asking whether you want to waste any more time with the kitchenmaid. You try to think of anything she might know.

- *If you checked Deduction 11,* ***turn to 498.***
- *Otherwise,* ***turn to 384.***

538

You chat a little with the butler. "I am surprised to hear of any of the aristocracy leaving town now," you say casually. "I would have thought she would have stayed in London for the Earl of Dovercourt's wedding."

"She decided to leave suddenly on the 14th, sir," the butler answers. "She said she had finally arranged matters here so that she could leave the city, and she felt she needed the change of air."

- *If you ask if something upset her to cause this decision,* ***turn to 248.***
- *Otherwise,* ***turn to 294.***

539

Though you were afraid of falling for a moment, you reach the ground safely and quietly. You cross the yard and vault the back wall. ***Pick a number:***

- *If 2-5,* ***turn to 536.***
- *If 6-12,* ***turn to 533.***

540

You crosscheck the people mentioned by Milverton's cook and secretary against the list of possible blackmail victims you assembled yesterday. Everyone mentioned by Milverton's employees is on your longer list. You wonder if it is worthwhile to take the time to talk to those not mentioned by either member of Milverton's household.

- *If you want to talk only to those mentioned by both the cook and the secretary,* ***turn to 622.***
- *If you want to talk only to those mentioned by either the cook or secretary,* ***turn to 230.***
- *If you want to talk to everyone you have noted as a possible blackmail victim,* ***turn to 363.***
- *If you want to visit only those mentioned by the secretary,* ***turn to 454.***
- *If you want to visit only those mentioned by the cook,* ***turn to 374.***

541

You find nothing hidden in or under any of the clothing, but then you realize that one drawer seems more shallow than it should be, while another is not as long as you would expect from the depth of the dresser. Closer examination uncovers a false bottom in the shallow drawer, while removal of the narrow one reveals a compartment hidden behind it. Both of these hiding places are empty, but they strengthen your view of Milverton as a man who had much to hide. ***Turn to 582.***

542

Holmes listens to your explanation of Lady Blakeney's guilt. "Well," he says, "you have established a connection between her Ladyship and Milverton, but you do not have any proof of her guilt."

•*If you wish to investigate the case again,* ***turn to 490.***
•*Otherwise,* ***turn to 616.***

543

You wonder why the undergardener gave up his pursuit of the intruders at the wall, rather than following them over.

•*If you ask him why he stopped,* ***turn to 347.***
•*If you are finished questioning Green,* ***turn to 146.***

544

"I don't know who locked the dog up last night," the butler snaps. "When I went to tell one of the men to do it, I found Brutus was already in the basement. I don't see any point in continuing this conversation." ***Turn to 268.***

545

Watson laughs even louder, and even Holmes smiles. "Do you think that the case would have reached its present state if we had been the men?" Holmes asks. "Though Milverton was one of the worst men in London, I hardly looked on his murder as a desirable late evening exercise for Watson and myself. Why, if I were engaged in such an activity, do you think I would take Watson along? He is the perfect companion for a dangerous mission, but not for burglary." Watson blushes as you laugh in agreement. ***Turn to 262.***

546

The ivy breaks in your hand, and you fall to the yard, yelling involuntarily as you do. Unhurt but frightened by the noise you made, you run to the back wall and vault over it. ***Pick a number:***

- *If 2-8,* ***turn to 536.***
- *If 9-12,* ***turn to 533.***

547

You consult your list and consider going to see Miss Miles and Colonel Dorking. Miss Miles is the most convenient to visit first.

- *If you visit her,* ***turn to 597.***
- *If you decide not to see her, but wish to see Colonel Dorking,* ***turn to 309.***
- *If you visit neither,* ***turn to 484.***

548

Holmes shakes his head. "I shall not answer that," he tells you. "I think I have made it clear that I would prefer to see the case remain unsolved. However, in general, if you search for a blackmailer, you should talk to people who might have been recent blackmail victims. Let us now talk of something more cheerful than murder." ***Turn to 277.***

549

The bath is neat, comfortable, and fitted with every modern convenience, as well as thick towels, fine soaps, and other paraphenalia. It is perfectly neat — obviously it hasn't been used since the maid cleaned it yesterday. You realize that its pristine condition indicates that Milverton never prepared to retire the night before. Lestrade agrees with your interpretation. *Check Deduction 4.* ***Turn to 160.***

5

550

You turn your thoughts away from the two intruders and consider other evidence. There seems to be a good chance that Milverton had another visitor, a woman, in addition to the men who fled after the killing. A busy night for a private study, you think grimly. If the visitor were a woman, she might be the killer! *Check Deduction 9.* ***Turn to 247.***

551

"Mrs. Lindon," you say gently, wishing she would stop crying, "could you tell me the routine for caring for Mr. Milverton and his rooms? When were they cleaned, and by whom? It might help us learn how the intruders carried out the crime."

Between sobs she replies: "Mr. Milverton was very particular about his rooms, sirs. The housemaid, Mary Jones, always cleaned the bedroom and bath in the afternoon. She worked on the study before that, while Mr. Jenkins was eating his lunch. Mr. Jenkins never left the room during the day, so if she cleaned while he was eating, she didn't disturb him at his work. Then, after dinner I went in, to be certain everything was neat and orderly the way he liked it: I turned down the covers and made sure the fire was laid. At half past nine, one of the footmen or the butler would light the fires, if Mr. Milverton wished it. It would be a bold man who would try to hide there until very late at night, after the household went to bed." She dabs her eyes again. Lestrade looks as if he wishes he had never seen the housekeeper. ***Turn to 259.***

552

"No," the peddler says, "I don't know no bloke named Escott, and I wouldn't tell you if I did. Now excuse me; I think that gent over there would like some of me flowers." He hurries off before you can reply. ***Turn to 516.***

553

The Constable takes you to the local police station. In the big, barren lobby an officer takes down your name and other information. You give him your letter from Inspector Lestrade, introducing you as his helper. Reluctantly, the officer agrees to send for the Inspector, and lets you wait in a small room rather than a cell.

Lestrade is furiously angry when he arrives."What's this?" he demands. "Burglary? I doubt Mr. Holmes taught you that was proper procedure."

"No," you admit, "it was foolish of me. But I believed I would find evidence there essential to the investigation, and I could hardly ask you to get a search warrant for that house."

"Evidence, you say," he replies, suddenly alert. "If you were breaking into Lady Blakeney's house to get evidence, I don't want to know a thing about what led you there. At least I was right in seeking private assistance — there are times when a little ignorance goes a long ways. For me, the case can remain unsolved, unless you feel that an arrest is essential."

"Then I can go?" you ask, surprised that you are not in for a long stretch in jail."

"Yes, you can go. I shall clear the arrest, so that you will not have to appear in court. My superiors will approve — they have told me to avoid scandal while investigating the murder." Before he can change his mind, you hurriedly leave the police station. ***Turn to 460.***

554

"I understand your relief," you say slowly. "Did you pay the villain?"

"No, I would have, if I had been able to raise it," she reples. "But it was simply out of the question — you cannot pay money that does not exist. And he refused to compromise. He believed that if he didn't get my money, the sudden cancellation of my wedding would make his other victims more willing to pay him." She shudders at the memory, and you wonder why she feels so safe. Her letters might still exist in someone else's hands.

•*If you ask her why she feels safe,* ***turn to 109.***
•*Otherwise,* ***turn to 184.***

555

"When we came here today, the dog was out in the yard barking loudly," you tell the undergardener. "I'm surprised that he didn't attack the intruders."

"Oh, most nights he would have," Green answers. "But he was locked in the basement when Mr. Milverton was killed."

"Why was he locked away?" you ask quickly.

"I don't know sir," he answers, "I just know he was. I let him out in the morning." ***Pick a number*** *and add your Intuition bonus:*

•*If 2-6,* ***turn to 305.***
•*If 7-12,* ***turn to 240.***

556

After supper, you consider whether or not to visit Sherlock Holmes and ask his opinion of the case. While too busy to investigate the case himself, he might find some connections between scraps of evidence.

•*If you visit Holmes at Baker Street,* ***turn to 315.***
•*Otherwise,* ***turn to 311.***

557

Holmes listens carefully to your explanation, then gives you a thin smile. "That is a very solid proof," he says. "There is little doubt that you are correct, and it would be difficult for anyone to refute your charges. You show signs of learning your trade." The compliment delights you. ***Turn to 616.*** 3

558

You decide it would be better not to waste Mr. Holmes' time by visiting him this evening. You pass the evening pondering the facts that you have gathered, wondering which of them have any significance. Then you sleep well and rise early the next morning, prepared to continue the investigation. ***Turn to 410.***

559

Appledore Towers is a rambling mansion, with the numerous garrets and other decorative features popular with modern architects. Extensive grounds surround the house, including a tree-filled park and formal gardens. A gravel drive runs from the gate to the main door. The fierce barking of a large dog concerns you for a moment, but your fears vanish when you see that the beast is securely leashed.

"As you can see, the house is very grand," Lestrade says. "Mr. Milverton did very well in his dealings as an 'agent'. We have changed nothing here, except that the body has been taken away to the morgue. I think you should examine the grounds first. There was a heavy frost last night, and the men left some marks behind them. They cannot last indefinitely with the sun growing stronger." You nod in agreement; Lestrade's suggestion makes good sense.

11

Then the detective introduces a man who is waiting just inside the gate. The stranger is a large, immensely dignified man, flawlessly dressed in the black suit of a butler. "This is Mr. Silversmith, Milverton's butler," Lestrade says. "He will accompany us, to answer any questions you have about the arrangement of the house and grounds." You thank the butler for his assistance and begin to study the area around the gates and driveway. ***Pick a number** and add your Observation bonus:*

•*If 2-5, **turn to 486.***
•*If 6-12, **turn to 522.***

560

You thank the page for his help, and watch him leave the room. ***Turn to 260.***

561

"John and James Patterson were the intruders," you say. "They must have wanted revenge and blamed Milverton for the loss of their income."

Holmes shakes his head. "There was a piece in the papers that their income was restored by their uncle. If they had wanted to kill Milverton, they would have done it long ago." ***Turn to 477.***

562

"Lady Eva Blackwell killed Milverton," you tell Holmes. "She desperately needed to do something to keep him from preventing her marriage."

"Nonsense," Holmes replies. "None of the evidence points towards her. Careful investigation would show that she was assured that she would be protected. And if you met the lady, I don't think she seemed the type who could empty a gun into a man." ***Turn to 352.***

563

From her appearance and demeanor, you realize that Mary Jones probably is more than a little bit of a flirt. You wonder whether her boyfriends ever visit her at the house.

•*If you ask about a boyfriend,* ***turn to 354.***
•*Otherwise,* ***turn to 366.***

564

You recognize that the pebbles came from the border of the driveway at Appledore Towers. You had found some of the pebbles in the woman's footprints leading away from the house, but not in the prints left by the men who fled. Perhaps the woman killed Milverton! *Check Deduction 9.*

•*If you checked Clue D,* ***turn to 406.***
•*Otherwise,* ***turn to 390.***

565

The housemaid is trembling as she explains in more detail where everyone had gone when Silversmith asked her to lock away Brutus.

"Calm yourself," you reply sharply, "don't go to all that trouble to make up such a pack of lies, girl, when we already know the truth. Silversmith told us he was ordered to have the dog locked up, but found that it already had been. Now tell us why you locked Brutus in the basement." ***Turn to 430.***

566

You wonder whether Jenkins has any idea who killed Milverton, and whether he would admit his master's ill deeds in order to name the murderer.

•*If you ask him who might have killed Milverton,* ***turn to 118.***
•*Otherwise,* ***turn to 442.***

567

You sigh, then say: "I do not know who the men were. I have not been able to figure it out."

•*If you want to investigate the case further,* ***turn to 490.***
•*If you want Holmes to explain, turn to* ***568.***

568

"My friend," Holmes says, "Dr. Watson and I were the two intruders in Appledore Towers. Don't look so surprised," he adds, noting your astonishment. "The evidence should have been obvious."

"What evidence?" you ask.

"Who else possessed the motive and the ability to open the safe?" Holmes asks. "You should have discovered that Milverton visited me, and that Lady Eva Blackwell employed me to deal with the villain. The cabbie who took Watson and I away from the Heath might have given you a good description. Then there's the fact that I was the plumber, Escott, who asked the maid to tie up the dog. I've spoken to you before about a dog that doesn't bark in the night. There was so much evidence that I'm surprised that even Lestrade didn't deduce the proper solution, much less you." ***Turn to 203.***

569

"Thank you, captain," you answer. "I need to know why your appointment as attache at Lisbon was cancelled so suddenly."

Grey's eyes flash angrily, and Fraser turns dark red in outrage. "Get out of here!" the Lieutenant orders. "I can see that you are some scandalmonger, using your letters of introduction to snoop into someone else's private affairs. Well, you shall not have such fun with my friend, I can tell you that!" As he reaches for a heavy walking stick, you hurriedly leave their quarters. ***Turn to 230.***

570

You look through the legal document. Disappointed, you find that it is a perfectly innocuous document dealing with the management of some of Milverton's property. You drop it back into the drawer where you found it. ***Turn to 216.***

571

"Milverton!" the Colonel shouts, "Do not mention that name in my household! Get out of my home! If I knew who killed Milverton, I would spend my last penny to help him escape!" The nephew looks as angry as the Colonel, and you leave in a hurry. ***Turn to 484.***

572

A cab drops you at the townhouse of the Countess. The butler takes your card, and returns quickly to lead you in to see the Countess. She is a tall, wiry woman, of late middle years, with a hard, lined face. You have a feeling that Milverton would have regretted any attempt to blackmail her.

"Good day, sir," she says very pleasantly. "It is nice of you to come and see me, although I cannot imagine what matter could bring a consulting detective to my door. I hope this isn't some petty little matter that will waste my time."

"Hardly a petty matter," you reply. "A man named Milverton was murdered. Because of the nature of his activities, it is necessary to talk to anyone mentioned in his papers. I am assisting the police in the case."

•*If you checked Decision 20,* ***turn to 284.***
•*Otherwise,* ***turn to 123.***

573

Jenkins hesitates a long time before answering you. "In the course of his business Mr. Milverton acquired many papers which might have embarassed the people named in them. You know what I mean, do you not?" he asks in a pleading voice.

"Just what do you mean?" you demand brusquely.

Jenkins sighs. "Many of the letters Mr. Milverton had in his safe named one person as the lover of another, or discussed other information best kept quiet. I certainly would not have thrown them into the fire myself, but as the intruders had done so, it seemed discreet to let them burn."

"I see," you reply, still studying Jenkins.

•*If you ask him who killed Milverton,* ***turn to 400.***
•*Otherwise,* ***turn to 442.***

574

"Who killed my master?" Jenkins repeats. "I have no idea who might have hated him that much. No, sir, no idea at all. But if he misused the letters he had, you would be able to find some suspects by looking through the recent papers, reviewing scandals, and then by discovering which scandal victims knew Mr. Milverton." ***Turn to 442.***

575

"Yes," Holmes continues, "it will be an impressive feat to identify the woman, but there is another more important question — do you want to identify her?"

"Mr. Holmes?" you ask, startled by the question. "I thought I explained my reasons for undertaking the investigation. Are they not valid?"

"Not necessarily," he answers. "If a woman murders a blackmailer, it stands to reason that she has suffered at his hands. Would you cause such a victim even more pain?"

•*If you agree with Holmes,* ***turn to 513.***
•*Otherwise,* ***turn to 252.***

576

You sup at your lodgings. You try to decide what you might do this evening to further your investigation. The only useful task that occurs to you would be another visit to see Mr. Holmes.

•*If you checked Clues N or O, but not E,* ***turn to 194.***
•*Otherwise,* ***turn to 558.***

577

The footman looks as if he might be a butler some day; he shares Silversmith's staid, calm features and neat clothes. When you ask him to tell what happened during the murder, he has his story ready.

"I was in bed," he begins, "almost asleep when the shots went off. I wondered for a moment whether it was my imagination, but then I heard everyone else up and shouting, so I pulled on my trousers and shoes and ran out to see what was happening.

"The butler was rousing all of us, and when he had everyone awake he led us around to the master's study, but we found the door locked, and that little passage didn't give us room to force it open. Then we ran around to the front door and out. As we came around from the outside, we saw two men come out of the study, run up the veranda and vanish into the garden. Mr. Silversmith spread us out and we commenced searching. I was on the left side of the line when Tommy Green shouted that he saw them, but when I come up to him, Tommy was lying at the foot of the wall, nursing his jaw. None of us fancied following a couple of armed men out across the open heath, especially as it was mortal cold. And that's all we saw, sir."

•*If you ask his opinion of Milverton,* ***turn to 173.***
•*Otherwise,* ***turn to 213.***

578

You hail a hansom and give the driver the address of Lady Sylvia's mansion. He listens, then says: "It's no use going to see the Lady, guv. She's been in Spain for the past two weeks, and isn't expected back for a few days yet, if I don't miss my guess. My cousin is her maid and travels with her." You thank the driver for saving you the trip, and tip him six pence (if you have it). *Deduct the money from your Character Record.* ***Turn to 169.***

579

"I actually heard your names mentioned, almost with reverence, by one of the staff," you go on. "The page, a boy named Johnny, assured me that Mr. Sherlock Holmes was the greatest detective the world had ever seen." Watson tries unsuccessfully to suppress his laughter; Holmes smiles thinly at the compliment. "But the boy told me the silliest story you ever heard."

"Oh?" Holmes asks, "That would have to be very silly indeed, as Dr. Watson can attest. I have heard some very odd talk in my time."

"The page says he saw the two men when they climbed the wall, and when he heard the description the undergardener gave of them, he concluded that you and Watson were the two men who fled the scene. Because he admires you, he at least did not believe that you murdered Milverton."

"That is some comfort," Holmes says, while Watson roars with laughter. "Though we hardly matched his faith if we were there and were unable to stop the murder, did we?"

•*If you ask if they were the men,* ***turn to 338.***
•*Otherwise,* ***turn to 262.***

580

"What did you think of Mr. Milverton?" you ask Yates. "What kind of man was he?"

"Oh, 'e were as good as you can 'ope for I guess," the groom answers. "'e paid better than most and never give a man trouble, but I didn't 'ardly know 'im to know what sort of man 'e were. Not 'ardly my station, you see. I just do my job and let the gentry live their lives without no interference from me." ***Turn to 234.***

581

"You are certain that the lady was justified?" you ask again. Holmes nods grimly and Watson warmly backs him up. "Very well," you say, "I shall quit the investigation."

"You have made a wise choice," Holmes answers. "I had pursued my trade for many years before I realized that sometimes the successful conclusion of a case produced much misery and little good." This case is over. **THE END.**

582

You wonder whether you should go through the clothes in Milverton's wardrobe.

•*If you search the wardrobe,* ***turn to 339.***
•*Otherwise,* ***turn to 403.***

583

"I did nothing improper," Jenkins says stiffly. "I am certain that the police were pleased that we had not disturbed the scene of the crime."

•*If you ask him who killed Milverton,* ***turn to 199.***
•*Otherwise,* ***turn to 421.***

584

"Well, my friend," Holmes says, "Dr. Watson and I actually were the two intruders at Appledore Towers. The proof was there, if you had looked hard enough for it."

"Please enlighten me," you prompt him.

"Who else possessed the motive and the ability to open the safe?" Holmes asks. "You might have discovered that Milverton visited me, and that Lady Eva Blackwell employed me to deal with the villain. The cabbie who took Watson and I away from the Heath on the night of the murder could have given you an excellent description of us. Then there is the fact that I was the plumber, Esscot, who asked the maid to tie up the dog. There was so much evidence, in fact, that I am surprised that even Lestrade didn't deduce the proper solution, much less you." ***Turn to 203.***

585

You consider your next question for Mrs. Lindon.

•*If you ask about the household routine,* ***turn to 551.***
•*If you let Mrs. Lindon leave,* ***turn to 259.***

586

You remember that Holmes often has experienced good fortune advertising in the agony columns of the popular newspapers when he had to find some unknown person, especially an ordinary working person. It will cost you 2 shillings for each newspaper to which you send your advertisement. *Deduct the cost for the number of newspapers you use from your Character Record. Note the number of newspapers on your Character Record.*

•*If you are using advertisements,* ***turn to 389.***
•*If you decide not to use advertisements,* ***turn to 290.***

587

You consider Silversmith's comments. "What did these papers look like?" you ask the butler. "Why were they burning in the fireplace after midnight?"

"They appeared to be letters," he replies carefully. "The fire was too hot to allow us to look at them closely."

"Why did you let them burn?" you ask quickly.

"That was Mr. Jenkins's decision," he answers more easily. "He said we shouldn't touch or change a thing in the room, lest we impede the Yard's efforts to discover who murdered the master." *Check Clue J.* ***Turn to 178.***

588

Holmes listens to you, then says: "You have shown that one of us was at Appledore Towers that night. If Watson or I were one of the intruders, it is safe to assume the identity of his companion." ***Turn to 203.***

589

"How did you get caught in such a situation?" you ask, eagerly. Both officers look sharply at you.

"Don't worry about it," Captain Gray says, obviously irritated. "It is not connected to your investigation."

•*If you ask him if he's heard of Milverton,* ***turn to 153.***
•*If you thank them and leave,* ***turn to 494.***

590

"Your delight in the murder interests me," you say slowly.

"If anyone had ever blackmailed you, you would be delighted at his passing," James Patterson answers back. "The killing was a definite public service."

"And where were you at the time of the public service?" you ask him. ***Pick a number*** *and add your Communication bonuus: (Add 3 if you checked Decision 20.)*

•*If 2-6,* ***turn to 440.***
•*If 7-12,* ***turn to 271.***

591

"Mr. Holmes," you answer, a little shyly, "I believe that you and Dr. Watson were the two mysterious intruders."

"Us?" Holmes asks in an astonished voice. "Surely you jest, and it is hardly a fit time for that." With Holmes and Watson staring at you, you hurriedly explain the evidence behind your deduction.

- *If you checked Clue Q and/or R, and at least one of Clues E, O and/or X,* ***turn to 317.***
- *If you checked Clue Q and/or R,* ***turn to 588.***
- *If you checked Clue E and/or O, and checked Clue X,* ***turn to 331.***
- *If you checked at least one of Clues E, and/or O, and/or X,* ***turn to 267.***
- *If you checked Clue N and/or Deduction 6,* ***turn to 395.***
- *Otherwise,* ***turn to 598.***

592

Watson laughs even louder, and even Holmes smiles. "Do you think that the case would have reached its present state if we had been the men?" Holmes asks. "Though Milverton was one of the worst men in London, I hardly looked on his murder as a desirable late evening exercise for Watson and myself." You laugh and agree. ***Turn to 262.***

593

You find nothing interesting in your examination of the bed. The covers have been folded back neatly and the pillows fluffed. ***Turn to 393.***

594

The tracks of the two men finally come to the wall that separates the grounds of Appledore Towers from Hampstead Heath. Here the tracks of one servant come up from a different angle, and end in marks indicating that the servant took a fall. The wall is strongly built of stone, about six feet tall. The top of the wall is covered with pieces of broken glass along most of its length. At the point where the tracks end, the glass has been knocked off the wall onto the ground on the other side. You realize that if anyone crossed the walls to enter the grounds, he must have dislodged some of this glass.

- *If you circle the walls to see if they were crossed at any other point,* ***turn to 382.***
- *If you cross the wall yourself and follow the intruders' trail across Hampstead Heath,* ***turn to 455.***

595

"What did Mr. Silversmith say was just a dream?" you ask very gently, for the boy is obviously a little scared and confused.

"Well, I heard so much from the others that I'm not sure what I saw and what was my dream before I woke up. I can't remember hearing the shots, but the noise might have gotten me out of bed without quite realizing it. You know how it is when something wakes you from a sound sleep. I seem to remember looking out the window, then, and seeing a cloaked lady hurrying away from the house towards the gates. After that I'm sure I fell back in bed — it's right by the window — and then woke again when the rest of the staff was chasing around the house."

- *If you ask about the two men,* ***turn to 189.***
- *Otherwise,* ***turn to 560.***

596

You sit in Milverton's chair and begin to go through his desk, opening the various drawers and compartments in turn, trying to be careful and methodical. Aside from the usual writing equipment, stationary and other paraphenalia one usually finds in a businessman's desk, you find something unexpected — a loaded gun. Two or three other legal documents similar to the one on top of the desk, some letters, and an appointment book fill the top drawer. Lestrade tenses with impatience as you glance at these things, then growls: "You're not going to read all those bloody papers, are you? It would take all day and half the night."

To avoid irritating him, you decide to read only one of them thoroughly.

•*If you look at one of the legal papers,* ***turn to 570.***
•*If you read a letter,* ***turn to 301.***
•*If you examine the appointment book,* ***turn to 600.***

597

You hurry to Miss Miles' address, a townhouse in the West End. After you send in your credentials, a maid shows you in to meet Miss Miles. You exchange greetings, while considering how to question her. She is a pleasant-looking, intelligent woman in her middle twenties.

•*If you say you are investigating blackmail,* ***turn to 237.***
•*If you ask if she heard of Milverton,* ***turn to 364.***

598

Holmes shakes his head. "You have no evidence at all. That is nothing but a guess. Poor work indeed."

•*If you investigate the case further,* ***turn to 490.***
•*If you would like Holmes to explain,* ***turn to 584.***
•*Otherwise,* ***turn to 203.***

4

599

"Well, Mr. Holmes," you begin, "I learned today that Mr. Milverton came to visit you recently. I hoped you might be able to tell me why and what happened."

Holmes shakes his head. "No, I don't think I can tell you that. His visit was too closely related to the private affairs of one of my clients. I will assure you that it had nothing to do with Milverton's murder." You nod, knowing better than to try to press Holmes on such a question.

•*If you checked Clue N,* ***turn to 579.***
•*Otherwise,* ***turn to 262.***

600

You pick up Milverton's appointment book and flip through it. By chance, it opens near the back. You shiver at the appointments for today and tomorrow and early next week, appointments that will never be fulfilled. Then you look at yesterday's notes. At noon Milverton met his solicitor; at six in the evening he visited a friend. Then you see another note:

Midnight, maid to Countess d'Albert—future business.

You read it to Lestrade "An odd time to have an appointment," the Inspector mutters, "and an odd person with whom to meet. Perhaps the maid had possession of papers compromising her mistress, and wanted a secret meeting." You nod in agreement. *Check Clue D.*

•*If you have checked Deduction 3,* ***turn to 270.***
•*Otherwise,* ***turn to 318.***

601

You consider Holmes' question.

•*If you say Holmes and Watson killed Milverton,* ***turn to 358.***

•*If you say someone else killed Milverton,* ***turn to 412.***

602

Impatient with all delays, Lestrade leads you along the veranda to the beginning of the suspects' trail. *Erase your check on Decision 1.* ***Turn to 381.***

603

"Miss Phillippa Blackwell killed Milverton," you say. "That woman would do anything to protect her cousin!"

Holmes shakes his head and says: "You have presented no evidence to point to her. Also, she had been assured that Lady Eva's interests would be protected." ***Turn to 352.***

604

"I discovered the gun and an incriminating note in her room," you explain.

"That is very convincing evidence by itself," Holmes says. "It proves both a motive and a method for the killing. What else have you learned?"

- *If you checked Clues D and Z, or Clue S and Decision 19, or either Clue K or Clue L,* ***turn to 615.***
- *Otherwise,* ***turn to 557.***

605

You begin your efforts by identifying the marks of each of the two men. You find that they wore some sort of rubber-soled shoes, and that the marks are not distinct enough to identify the men. By studying the marks of each man you realize that one of them was tall with a long stride while the other was probably medium-sized, with a noticeably shorter stride. You can tell nothing else from the marks. ***Turn to 594.***

606

You try to explain the evidence completely.

- *If you checked Clues K, L or Z,* ***turn to 614.***
- *Otherwise,* ***turn to 611.***

607

"Mr. Milverton was a good master," Mrs. Lindon says slowly. "He paid us well and never complained unless he had a reason; he always let us know in advance if he wanted us to do anything special. Oh, this is such a terrible thing, I can't imagine why someone would kill him." She dabs at here eyes with a handkerchief. ***Turn to 585.***

608

Jenkins is obviously a careful and discreet man. You wonder if he would tell you anything of his master's business, now that his master is dead.

•*If you ask about Milverton's business,* ***turn to 117.***
•*Otherwise,* ***turn to 566.***

609

"Want to kill him?" Mrs. Lindon reiterates. "He was a hard-working man who took good care of us. And in spite of his good nature, there's folk who talked about him behind his back, as though he'd try to do harm to anyone. It's these immoral people who think they're so high and mighty," she goes on, "they're the ones at fault, and then they blame a poor innocent man when their scandalous behaviour comes home to them."

"Now Mrs. Lindon, calm yourself," you say, making soothing motions with your hand. "No one is making accusations against Mr. Milverton."

"Indeed you are!" she snaps back. "You're thinking them anyway, trying to find justification for the killers."

•*If you ask her about her household routine,* ***turn to 251.***
•*Otherwise,* ***turn to 259.***

610

You thank Bessie for her help. She obviously knows nothing that will help you in your investigation. ***Turn to 344.***

611

"You must have more proof than that," Holmes says. "You have made a serious accusation."

•*If you checked Decision 19 and Clue S,* ***turn to 542.***
•*Otherwise,* ***turn to 204.***

612

You study Mary Jones carefully. "You said you were crying and so didn't hear the gunshots," you begin. "Why were you crying? Did Mr. Milverton or the housekeeper cause your discomfort?"

She doesn't reply for a while, and you wonder if you should have asked. "I don't know what it has to do with the murder, sir," she begins reluctantly.

"We don't know what anything has to do with the murder," you answer gently. "Now wouldn't you like to be certain it was not connected to the killing?"

She smiles. "It was this way, sir," she says. "I just got engaged this week, to a man I met, and he was supposed to come and visit me that night; he never did come, and I haven't had a word from him since."

"How long had you known him?" you ask.

"Oh, only a fortnight. He was so charming, and a plumber with a good growing business, sir. He did work for the gas company." You consider the best way to learn more.

- *If you ask her if she locked the dog up for her boyfriend,* ***turn to 443.***
- *Otherwise,* ***turn to 207.***

613

You identify the marks of each of the two men. You find that they wore rubber-soled shoes, and that the marks are not distinct enough to identify the men. By studying the marks of each man you realize that one of them was tall with a long stride while the other was probably of medium height with a shorter stride. As you trace their path to the wall it becomes clear that the taller man was in front of the other man, since the shorter man's marks overlap the other's in a number of places.

As you near the wall you turn and look back towards the house. You are impressed immediately by the taller man's knowledge of the grounds of Appledore Towers. Though running in the dark, the tall man chose a route that used the available cover effectively, and also led the other man to the wall as quickly as possible. ***Turn to 594.***

614

Holmes listens as you continue to explain how you reached your conclusions.

- *If you checked Clue D and Clue Z, or Clue S and Decision 19,* ***turn to 557.***
- *Otherwise,* ***turn to 542.***

615

Holmes listens to your explanation, then nods. "That is about as thorough an explanation of the case as could be presented. You have done an excellent job in this case." You smile with his kind words. ***Turn to 616.***

616

Holmes continues to speak. "You know now who killed Milverton," he says, "but I cannot permit you to reveal your success to anyone else. I do not think Lady Blakeney should be prosecuted for her crime. She suffered irreparable harm from Milverton's actions, and legal methods would have provided only a token repayment for her wrongs. To prosecute her would ruin her, and she does not deserve that. I will hold you to our agreement — do not tell Lestrade who killed him."

"But what will that do to my career?" you ask. "And what will Lestrade say or do to me?"

"I will see Lestrade," Holmes continues, "And without telling him any details, I will make it clear to him that he does not want to know who killed Milverton. A trial of Lady Blakeney would rock the country." You accept Holmes' demand and agree to keep the secret. After some further discussion of the case, you leave Baker Street. Already, you are eagerly wondering what sort of crime will provide the impetus for your next investigation. **THE END.**

617

You cannot think of any method to approach the Countess, other than by relying on your own tact and Lestrade's letter of introduction. Perhaps the Countess will see the advantage of leaving the police out of the matter. ***Turn to 572.***

618

As you order the evidence in your mind, you realize that the two men must have entered the study, opened the safe, then hid behind the curtains when Milverton came into the room, and remained hidden for a long time.

•*If you checked Clues B, or Clues B & D,* ***turn to 220.***
•*If you checked Clue AA or Clue D,* ***turn to 550.***
•*Otherwise,* ***turn to 247.***

619

You thank Yates for his help, and he tugs his cap and leaves, happy to be done with the talk. ***Turn to 474.***

620

Again the next day you rise early in the morning, ready to continue your pursuit of the murderer. You feel confident that today you may confront the murderer, face to face. Of course, you will have to identify him as well, but that problem does not concern you deeply.

•*If you checked Decision 14 and did not check Clue R or U,* ***turn to 176.***
•*If you checked Decision 15 and did not check Clue S,* ***turn to 507.***
•*Otherwise,* ***turn to 385.***

621

"Escott," the foreman mutters, "Escott? No, I can't say I ever heard the name, sir. You must have been misinformed by someone, sir, he did no work for us." You thank the foreman for his time and leave. ***Turn to 142.***

622

You decide that it is only worthwhile to talk to the possible victims mentioned by both Milverton's secretary and his cook. *Check Decision 17.* ***Turn to 374.***

623

You turn your attention to Milverton's desk. The marks of blood on the desktop show that Milverton fell across the desk at some point in his suffering. Many of the papers on the desk are crumpled, as though the dying man grabbed at them in his agony. A cigar, smoked near to its end, sits in an ashtray. Its butt shows that it burned out and was not put out by its smoker. A legal document lies among the other papers. The arrangement of its sheets indicates that it was put down partially read. ***Pick a number*** *and add your Intuition bonus:*

•*If 2-6,* ***turn to 447.***
•*If 7-12,* ***turn to 253.***

624

"The housemaid, Mary Jones, is next on my list," Lestrade comments. "You see why I hate murders in these houses filled with servants don't you?" he adds with a laugh. "Do you want to see this Jones girl?"

•*If you see Mary Jones,* ***turn to 314.***
•*Otherwise,* ***turn to 126.***

625

"How was your embarassment arranged?" you ask slowly. "I do not mean to pry, but my case involves a man who often benefited from scandals and embarassments."

"I'm afraid it did not take anyone expert to trap me," Gray says bitterly. "Hear a sad tale as a lesson for your future. Tell him, Fraser; it makes me sick to think of it."

The lieutenant nods. "It was this way," he begins. "The other possible candidate for attache was Captain Felix Martin, a friend of ours and a good man. When the General chose Grey, he told Martin's family that he considered him equally qualified. A few days later, they invited Grey to spend a weekend with them at their place in the country. Late in the evening, as he was undressing, my friend heard a cry and a crash from the room occupied by one of Martin's sisters. He hurried over, knocked at the door, and when he got no answer went in to find the girl sprawled on the floor, apparently unconscious. He lifted her gently to lay her on the bed when her father burst in, and the girl came to life giggling just as her father arrived. They passed the story on to the General, and Grey's appointment was cancelled by the end of the next week."

"I'm probably lucky I didn't end up married to the girl," Grey mutters. "I think it was her idea, not her father's or brother's, and she didn't really understand the harm she did. She just wished to help her brother." You express your outrage and sympathy against such a terrible injustice. ***Turn to 494.***

626

You consider the secretary's careful statement, and wonder if he told Silversmith to let the papers burn.

•*If you ask why he let the papers burn,* ***turn to 391.***
•*Otherwise,* ***turn to 608.***

627

"Could you tell me about the watchdog?" you ask tentatively. "What hours did he run loose and who took care of him, who could lock him up, and so on?"

The butler considers the question. "Brutus was let loose around sundown, and had the freedom of the grounds until breakfast. The night of the murder, Mr. Milverton asked me to have him locked up, but didn't say why. When I went to tell Green to do it, I realized the dog was already in the cellar, so I didn't bother."

"Who could have locked him up besides Green?" you ask.

"Yates, the groom, also took care of him, and Brutus obeyed Mary Jones, the housemaid. I think Helen, the kitchenmaid could lock him up too — she feeds him. No one else would dare." *Check Deduction 11 and Clue I.* ***Turn to 268.***

628

What can you do to make important people talk to you?

•*If you checked Decision 20,* ***turn to 388.***
•*Otherwise,* ***turn to 416.***

WE NEED YOUR FEEDBACK!

PLEASE HELP US DO A BETTER JOB ON FUTURE BOOKS BY ANSWERING SOME OR ALL OF THE FOLLOWING QUESTIONS & SENDING YOUR REPLIES TO I.C.E.:

I purchased this book at ______________________________ ______________________________(name of store).

The name of this book is ______________________________ ______________________________.

I am (male/female) ____________, and ____________ years of age. I am in the ____________ grade in school.

I live in a (small, medium, large) ________________ town/city.

My favorite magazine is ______________________________.

I heard about this gamebook through ________________ ____________________ (a friend, a family member, an advertisement, other ____________________).

The one thing I like the *most* about this Sherlock Holmes Solo Mystery is ______________________________ ______________________________ ______________________________.

The one thing I like the *least* about this Sherlock Holmes Solo Mystery is ______________________________ ______________________________ ______________________________.

Send all feedback replies to:

IRON CROWN ENTERPRISES
P.O. BOX 1605, DEPT., SH
CHARLOTTESVILLE, VA. 22902